Ikenaga 2 Jos Leys

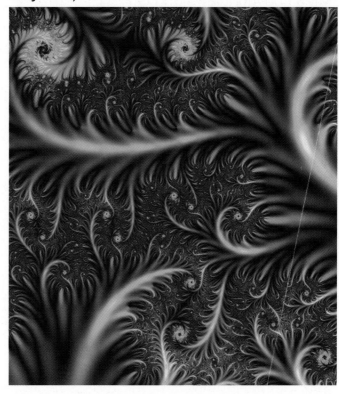

"A relatively simple formula can generate immensely complex images."– **Jos Leys**

Investigations
IN NUMBER, DATA, AND SPACE®

Glenview, Illinois • Boston, Massachusetts
Chandler, Arizona • Upper Saddle River, New Jersey

The Investigations curriculum was developed by TERC, Cambridge, MA.

This material is based on work supported by the National Science Foundation ("NSF") under Grant No. ESI-0095450. Any opinions, findings, and conclusions or recommendations expressed in this material are those of the author(s) and do not necessarily reflect the views of the National Science Foundation.

ISBN-13: 978-0-328-60026-7

ISBN-10: 0-328-60026-1

1 2 3 4 5 6 7 8 9 10 V003 14 13 12 11 10

T E R C

Co-Principal Investigators

Susan Jo Russell

Karen Economopoulos

Authors

Lucy Wittenberg
Director Grades 3–5

Karen Economopoulos
Director Grades K–2

Virginia Bastable
(SummerMath for Teachers,
Mt. Holyoke College)

Katie Hickey Bloomfield

Keith Cochran

Darrell Earnest

Arusha Hollister

Nancy Horowitz

Erin Leidl

Megan Murray

Young Oh

Beth W. Perry

Susan Jo Russell

Deborah Schifter
(Education
Development Center)

Kathy Sillman

Administrative Staff

Amy Taber
Project Manager

Beth Bergeron

Lorraine Brooks

Emi Fujiwara

Contributing Authors

Denise Baumann

Jennifer DiBrienza

Hollee Freeman

Paula Hooper

Jan Mokros

Stephen Monk
(University of Washington)

Mary Beth O'Connor

Judy Storeygard

Cornelia Tierney

Elizabeth Van Cleef

Carol Wright

Technology

Jim Hammerman

Classroom Field Work

Amy Appell

Rachel E. Davis

Traci Higgins

Julia Thompson

Collaborating Teachers

This group of dedicated teachers carried out extensive field testing in their classrooms, met regularly to discuss issues of teaching and learning mathematics, provided feedback to staff, welcomed staff into their classrooms to document students' work, and contributed both suggestions and written material that has been incorporated into the curriculum.

Bethany Altchek

Linda Amaral

Kimberly Beauregard

Barbara Bernard

Nancy Buell

Rose Christiansen

Chris Colbath-Hess

Lisette Colon

Kim Cook

Frances Cooper

Kathleen Drew

Rebeka Eston Salemi

Thomas Fisher

Michael Flynn

Holly Ghazey

Susan Gillis

Danielle Harrington

Elaine Herzog

Francine Hiller

Kirsten Lee Howard

Liliana Klass

Leslie Kramer

Melissa Lee Andrichak

Kelley Lee Sadowski

Jennifer Levitan

Mary Lou LoVecchio

Kristen McEnaney

Maura McGrail

Kathe Millett

Florence Molyneaux

Amy Monkiewicz

Elizabeth Monopoli

Carol Murray

Robyn Musser

Christine Norrman

Deborah O'Brien

Timothy O'Connor

Anne Marie O'Reilly

Mark Paige

Margaret Riddle

Karen Schweitzer

Elisabeth Seyferth

Susan Smith

Debra Sorvillo

Shoshanah Starr

Janice Szymaszek

Karen Tobin

JoAnn Trauschke

Ana Vaisenstein

Yvonne Watson

Michelle Woods

Mary Wright

Note: Unless otherwise noted, all contributors listed above were staff of the Education Research Collaborative at TERC during their work on the curriculum. Other affiliations during the time of development are listed.

Advisors

Deborah Lowenberg Ball,
University of Michigan

Hyman Bass, Professor of Mathematics and Mathematics Education
University of Michigan

Mary Canner, Principal, Natick Public Schools

Thomas Carpenter, Professor of Curriculum and Instruction,
University of Wisconsin-Madison

Janis Freckmann, Elementary Mathematics Coordinator,
Milwaukee Public Schools

Lynne Godfrey, Mathematics Coach,
Cambridge Public Schools

Ginger Hanlon, Instructional Specialist in Mathematics,
New York City Public Schools

DeAnn Huinker, Director, Center for Mathematics and
Science Education Research, University of Wisconsin-Milwaukee

James Kaput, Professor of Mathematics, University of
Massachusetts-Dartmouth

Kate Kline, Associate Professor, Department of Mathematics
and Statistics, Western Michigan University

Jim Lewis, Professor of Mathematics,
University of Nebraska-Lincoln

William McCallum, Professor of Mathematics,
University of Arizona

Harriet Pollatsek, Professor of Mathematics,
Mount Holyoke College

Debra Shein-Gerson, Elementary Mathematics Specialist,
Weston Public Schools

Gary Shevell, Assistant Principal,
New York City Public Schools

Liz Sweeney, Elementary Math Department,
Boston Public Schools

Lucy West, Consultant, Metamorphosis:
Teaching Learning Communities, Inc.

This revision of the curriculum was built on the work of the many authors who contributed to the first edition (published between 1994 and 1998). We acknowledge the critical contributions of these authors in developing the content and pedagogy of *Investigations*:

Authors

Joan Akers

Michael T. Battista

Douglas H. Clements

Karen Economopoulos

Marlene Kliman

Jan Mokros

Megan Murray

Ricardo Nemirovsky

Andee Rubin

Susan Jo Russell

Cornelia Tierney

Contributing Authors

Mary Berle-Carman

Rebecca B. Corwin

Rebeka Eston

Claryce Evans

Anne Goodrow

Cliff Konold

Chris Mainhart

Sue McMillen

Jerrie Moffet

Tracy Noble

Kim O'Neil

Mark Ogonowski

Julie Sarama

Amy Shulman Weinberg

Margie Singer

Virginia Woolley

Tracey Wright

Contents

UNIT 7

Finding Fair Shares

Investigations

CURRICULUM

Overview of Program Components

The **Curriculum Units** are the teaching guides. (See far right.)

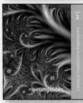

Implementing Investigations in Grade 3 offers suggestions for implementing the curriculum. It also contains a comprehensive index.

The **Differentiation and Intervention Guide** offers additional activities for each Investigation to support the range of learners.

Investigations for the Interactive Whiteboard provides whole-class instructional support to enhance each session.

The **Resource Masters and Transparencies CD** contains all reproducible materials that support instruction. The **LogoPaths CD** provides an environment in which students investigate a variety of geometric ideas.

The **Student Activity Book** contains the consumable student pages (Recording Sheets, Homework, Practice, and so on).

The **Student Math Handbook** contains Math Words and Ideas pages and Games directions.

The *Investigations* Curriculum

Investigations in Number, Data, and Space® is a K–5 mathematics curriculum designed to engage students in making sense of mathematical ideas. Six major goals guided the development of the *Investigations in Number, Data, and Space*® curriculum. The curriculum is designed to:

- Support students to make sense of mathematics and learn that they can be mathematical thinkers

- Focus on computational fluency with whole numbers as a major goal of the elementary grades

- Provide substantive work in important areas of mathematics—rational numbers, geometry, measurement, data, and early algebra—and connections among them

- Emphasize reasoning about mathematical ideas

- Communicate mathematics content and pedagogy to teachers

- Engage the range of learners in understanding mathematics

Underlying these goals are three guiding principles that are touchstones for the *Investigations* team as we approach both students and teachers as agents of their own learning:

1. *Students have mathematical ideas.* Students come to school with ideas about numbers, shapes, measurements, patterns, and data. If given the opportunity to learn in an environment that stresses making sense of mathematics, students build on the ideas they already have and learn about new mathematics they have never encountered. Students learn that they are capable of having mathematical ideas, applying what they know to new situations, and thinking and reasoning about unfamiliar problems.

2. *Teachers are engaged in ongoing learning* about mathematics content, pedagogy, and student learning. The curriculum provides material for professional development, to be used by teachers individually or in groups, that supports teachers' continued learning as they use the curriculum over several years. The *Investigations* curriculum materials are designed as much to be a dialogue with teachers as to be a core of content for students.

3. *Teachers collaborate with the students and curriculum materials* to create the curriculum as enacted in the classroom. The only way for a good curriculum to be used well is for teachers to be active participants in implementing it. Teachers use the curriculum to maintain a clear, focused, and coherent agenda for mathematics teaching. At the same time, they observe and listen carefully to students, try to understand how they are thinking, and make teaching decisions based on these observations.

Investigations is based on experience from research and practice, including field testing that involved documentation of thousands of hours in classrooms, observations of students, input from teachers, and analysis of student work. As a result, the curriculum addresses the learning needs of real students in a wide range of classrooms and communities. The investigations are carefully designed to invite all students into mathematics—girls and boys; members of diverse cultural, ethnic, and language groups; and students with a wide variety of strengths, needs, and interests.

Based on this extensive classroom testing, the curriculum takes seriously the time students need to develop a strong conceptual foundation and skills based on that foundation. Each curriculum unit focuses on an area of content in depth, providing time for students to develop and practice ideas across a variety of activities and contexts that build on each other. Daily guidelines for time spent on class sessions, Classroom Routines (K–3), and Ten-Minute Math (3–5) reflect the commitment to devoting adequate time to mathematics in each school day.

About This Curriculum Unit

This **Curriculum Unit** is one of nine teaching guides in Grade 3. The seventh unit in Grade 3 is *Finding Fair Shares*.

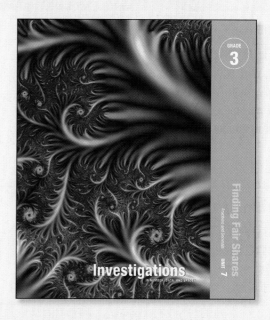

- The **Introduction and Overview** section organizes and presents the instructional materials, provides background information, and highlights important features specific to this unit.

- Each Curriculum Unit contains several **Investigations.** Each Investigation focuses on a set of related mathematical ideas.

- Investigations are divided into one-hour **Sessions,** or lessons.

- Sessions have a combination of these parts: **Activity, Discussion, Math Workshop, Assessment Activity,** and **Session Follow-Up.**

- Each session also has one or more **Classroom Routines** and **Ten-Minute Math** activities that are done outside of math time.

- At the back of the book is a collection of **Teacher Notes** and **Dialogue Boxes** that provide professional development related to the unit.

- Also included at the back of the book are the **Student Math Handbook** pages for this unit.

- The **Index** provides a way to look up important words or terms.

Overview

OF THIS UNIT

Investigation	Session	Day	
INVESTIGATION 1 **Sharing Brownies** Students work with unit fractions, looking at parts that make up a single whole as well as sets of objects that are a fraction of a group. Students also begin to use fractions with numerators greater than one.	**1.1** Making Fair Shares	1	
	1.2 Making Fraction Sets	2	
	1.3 More Than One Piece	3	
	1.4 Sharing Many Things	4	
	1.5 Sharing Several Brownies	5	
	1.6 Assessment: Sharing Four Brownies	6	
INVESTIGATION 2 **Many Ways to Make a Share** Students build their knowledge of fraction equivalencies as they represent whole and fractional quantities with pattern blocks.	**2.1** Making Cookie Shares	7	
	2.2 The Fraction Cookie Game	8	
	2.3 Assessment: Many Ways to Make a Share	9	
	2.4 Making Half-Yellow Designs	10	
INVESTIGATION 3 **Introduction to Decimals** Students are introduced to decimals (0.50 and 0.25) in the context of money. They compare decimals with their fractional equivalents, continuing to build a repertoire of notations to represent equivalent quantities.	**3.1** Sharing Money	11	
	3.2 Decimals on a Calculator	12	
	3.3 Fractions and Decimals That Are Equal	13	
	3.4 End-of-Unit Assessment	14	

Each *Investigations* session has some combination of these five parts: **Activity, Discussion, Math Workshop, Assessment Activity,** and **Session Follow-Up.** These session parts are indicated in the chart below. Each session also has one **Classroom Routine or Ten-Minute Math** activity that is done outside of math time.

 (W) Interactive Whiteboard

Activity	Discussion	Math Workshop	Assessment Activity	Session Follow-Up
●	(W)			●
(W)(W)	(W)			●
(W)●	(W)			●
(W)●	(W)			●
(W)●	●			●
(W)	(W)		●	●
(W)(W)	●			●
(W)●	(W)			●
	(W)	●	●	●
(W)		●		●
●●	(W)			●
	●	●		●
	(W)	●		●
			●	●

Ten-Minute Math

Today's Number	What Time Is It?
(W)	
(W)	
(W)	
	(W)
	(W)
	(W)
(W)	
(W)	
(W)	
(W)	
	(W)
	(W)
	(W)
	(W)

Mathematics

IN THIS UNIT

Finding Fair Shares is the Grade 3 unit in the rational number strand of *Investigations*. These units develop ideas about understanding, representing, and combining fractions and decimals.

LOOKING BACK In Grade 2, students began to develop an understanding of what fractions are and how they can be used to name quantities. Through working on problems about equal shares of a single object or of a set of objects, students worked with halves, thirds, and fourths. They also worked with these fractions in contexts of linear measurement and telling time (a length of $5\frac{1}{4}$ units, a time of half an hour). Students worked on the ideas that fractions refer to some number of equal parts of a whole; that is, one half is one of two equal parts, and the two parts together make up one whole (and one third is one of three equal parts, and so on). Students learned how the notation and words for fractions (e.g., $\frac{2}{3}$, two thirds) related to the meaning of these numbers. They also encountered mixed numbers, such as $1\frac{1}{2}$, to represent equal shares greater than one. Students worked with a small set of fractions and focused on two big ideas: that a fraction represents a part of a whole, and that the part it represents is one or more *equal* parts which together make the whole. In Grade 3, as students expand the fractions they use and work with more challenging problems, students will continue to work on these central ideas about fractions.

This unit focuses on 2 Mathematical Emphases:

1 **Rational Numbers** **Understanding the meaning of fractions (halves, fourths, eighths, thirds, sixths) and decimal fractions (0.50, 0.25) as equal parts of a whole (an object, an area, a set of objects)**

Math Focus Points

◆ Finding equal parts of a whole and naming them with fractions

◆ Dividing an area into equal parts

◆ Naming fractional parts with unit fractions ($\frac{1}{2}$, $\frac{1}{3}$, $\frac{1}{4}$, etc.)

◆ Ordering unit fractions

◆ Demonstrating that different-shaped pieces that are the same fraction of the same area have equal areas

◆ Naming fractional parts with fractions that have numerators greater than 1 ($\frac{3}{4}$, $\frac{2}{3}$, $\frac{3}{6}$, etc.)

◆ Dividing a group into equal parts and naming the parts with fractions

◆ Identifying equivalent fractional parts

◆ Using fraction notation to record equivalencies (e.g., $\frac{3}{6} = \frac{1}{2}$, $\frac{1}{2} = \frac{2}{4}$)

◆ Using mixed numbers to represent quantities greater than 1

◆ Identifying equivalent fractions and decimals for values involving halves and fourths (e.g., $\frac{1}{2} = 0.50$, $\frac{1}{4} = 0.25$, $2\frac{1}{2} = 2.5$)

◆ Reading, writing, and interpreting the meaning of the decimal numbers 0.50, 0.25, and numbers greater than 1 with these decimal portions, such as 2.5 and 2.25

Students need to understand the meaning of fractions and their relationships, just as they need number sense with whole numbers. Before learning to compute with fractions, they must do extensive work to understand what a fraction is (see **Teacher Note:** Why Are Fractions Difficult?: Developing Meaning for Fractions, page 109). Using a variety of contexts—rectangles representing "brownies," pattern block "cookies," and groups of objects—students learn how fractions are used to represent equal parts of a whole. In Grade 3, students work with halves, fourths, eighths, thirds, and sixths. They deepen the understanding they began to develop in Grade 2 that a fraction is a number that represents a relationship between two numbers and, in the fair-share contexts of this unit, that a fraction can be interpreted only in relation to a whole. The whole can be a single object ($\frac{1}{3}$ of a brownie), an area ($\frac{1}{3}$ of the surface of a hexagonal pattern block), or a group of things ($\frac{1}{3}$ of the class). One third of that whole is one of three equal parts; two thirds of that whole is two of the three equal parts; three thirds of that whole is three of the three equal parts, or one whole.

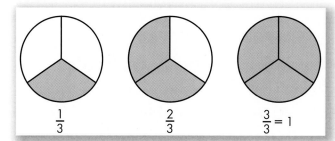

Students learn the meanings of the numerator and denominator of a fraction. For example, when comparing unit fractions (fractions with a numerator of 1), the fraction with the larger denominator is a smaller part of the whole: $\frac{1}{6}$ is smaller than $\frac{1}{2}$ of the same whole.

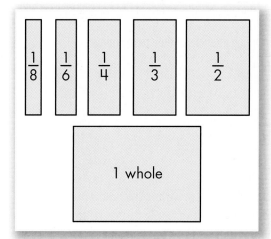

Students also gain experience with commonly used fractions and their equivalencies (e.g., three sixths and two fourths are both equal to one half of the same whole). Students leave this unit with strong mental images of many of these common equivalencies.

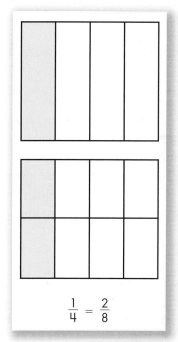

Through problems that involve dividing a group of things into equal shares (divide seven brownies among four people), students learn to use fractions and mixed numbers to represent quantities greater than one. They learn the words and fraction notation that represent the fractions they use in the unit.

In Investigation 3, students are introduced to a few decimal fractions (0.50 and 0.25) in the context of money, and gain familiarity with fraction and decimal equivalents involving halves and fourths. There is no benchmark for work with decimals in Grade 3; there will be extensive work with decimal fractions in Grades 4 and 5.

2 Rational Numbers Using representations to combine fractions (halves, fourths, eighths, thirds, and sixths)

Math Focus Points

◆ Using representations to combine fractions that sum to 1 (e.g., $\frac{1}{4} + \frac{3}{4} = 1, \frac{1}{3} + \frac{1}{3} + \frac{1}{3} = 1, \frac{1}{2} + \frac{1}{4} + \frac{1}{4} = 1$)

◆ Using representations to combine fractions to equal other fractions ($\frac{1}{2} = \frac{1}{3} + \frac{1}{6}$)

Fraction sense is based on the development of visual images of equivalent fractions, especially relationships among halves, fourths, and eighths and among halves, thirds, and sixths. Using understanding of these equivalents in the contexts of rectangular "brownies," pattern blocks, and groups of things, students find combinations of fractions that are equivalent to a whole or to another fraction (e.g., $\frac{1}{2} + \frac{2}{6} + \frac{1}{6} = 1, \frac{1}{3} + \frac{1}{6} = \frac{1}{2}$).

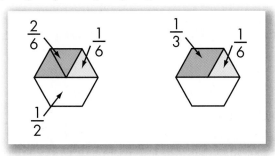

As students develop mental images for fraction relationships, from the contexts with which they work in the unit, they learn to reason about equivalencies and combinations of fractions. For example, to determine whether $\frac{1}{2} + \frac{1}{3}$ is more or less than 1, a student may say, "I know that $\frac{1}{2} + \frac{1}{2} = 1$, and because $\frac{1}{3}$ is less than $\frac{1}{2}$, $\frac{1}{2} + \frac{1}{3}$ has to be less than 1." Another student may say, "I know from the pattern blocks that $\frac{1}{3} + \frac{1}{6} = \frac{1}{2}$, so you'd need one more half to make 1: $\frac{1}{2} + \frac{1}{3} + \frac{1}{6} = 1$."

Classroom Routines focus on

◆ Learning about temperature: reading a thermometer, learning to associate different temperatures with words like colder and warmer, and establishing landmark temperatures

◆ Recording information in a table and on a graph

◆ Reading information from the shape of a graph: hot, cold, increasing, decreasing

Ten-Minute Math activities focus on

◆ Generating equivalent expressions for a number using particular constraints

◆ Practicing computation skills

◆ Using notation to record expressions

◆ Telling time to any minute on a digital or analog clock

◆ Determining intervals of time to the minute

LOOKING FORWARD In Grades 4 and 5, students continue to use representations and contexts to develop their understanding of the meaning of fractions and decimal fractions. Students compare and combine fractions but work with more challenging numerical relationships. For example, compare $\frac{3}{8}$ and $\frac{1}{3}$: Which fraction is greater? Which is closer to $\frac{1}{2}$? What is their sum? What is the difference between each fraction and 1? Students work more extensively with the idea of a fraction as a *number,* representing fractions and decimal fractions on a number line. They focus on the relationships among fractions, decimals, and percents; develop repertoires of equivalents; and use fractions, decimals, and percents in a variety of problem situations.

Using the *LogoPaths* Software   If you are using the *LogoPaths* software this year, give students ongoing access to computers outside of math time during this unit. *LogoPaths: Missing Measures* (M1–M2); and *LogoPaths: 340 Steps; 460 Steps; 520 Steps* (M3–M5) offer continued work with *Missing Measures* and the *Steps* activities. Students can also continue to play *Get the Toys* and *Feed the Turtle* and can spend time with the *Free Explore* option.

Assessment

IN THIS UNIT

ONGOING ASSESSMENT: Observing Students at Work

The following sessions provide **Ongoing Assessment: Observing Students at Work** opportunities:

- **Session 1.1, p. 26**
- **Session 1.2, pp. 31 and 33**
- **Session 1.3, pp. 38 and 40**
- **Session 1.4, p. 45**
- **Session 1.5, pp. 49 and 52**
- **Session 1.6, pp. 54 and 56**
- **Session 2.1, pp. 63 and 65**
- **Session 2.2, pp. 71–72**
- **Session 2.3, p. 78**
- **Session 2.4, p. 84**
- **Session 3.1, pp. 92 and 95**
- **Session 3.2, pp. 100 and 101**
- **Session 3.4, p. 108**

WRITING OPPORTUNITIES

The following sessions have **writing** opportunities for students to explain their mathematical thinking:

- **Session 1.5, p. 48**
  Student Activity Book, p. 11
- **Session 1.6, p. 56**
  M13, Assessment: Sharing Four Brownies
- **Session 2.2, p. 73**
  Student Activity Book, p. 21
- **Session 3.2, p. 101**
  Student Activity Book, p. 35
- **Session 3.4, p. 107**
  M19, End-of-Unit Assessment

PORTFOLIO OPPORTUNITIES

The following sessions have work appropriate for a **portfolio:**

- **Session 1.5, p. 51**
  M12, Sharing Several Brownies
- **Session 1.6, p. 54**
  Student Activity Book, pp. 15–16
- **Session 1.6, p. 56**
  M13, Assessment: Sharing Four Brownies
- **Session 2.3, p. 76**
  Student Activity Book, p. 23
- **Session 3.2, p. 100**
  Student Activity Book, pp. 33–34
- **Session 3.4, p. 107**
  M19, End-of-Unit Assessment

Assessing the Benchmarks

Observing students as they engage in conversation about their ideas is a primary means to assess their mathematical understanding. Consider all of your students' work, not just the written assessments. See the chart below for suggestions about key activities to observe.

See the **Differentiation and Intervention Guide** for quizzes that can be used after each Investigation.

Benchmarks in This Unit	Key Activities to Observe	Assessment
1. Divide a single whole or a quantity into equal parts, and name those parts as fractions or mixed numbers.	**Session 1.2:** Making Fraction Sets	**Session 1.6 Assessment Activity:** Sharing Four Brownies **Session 3.4 Assessment Activity:** End-of-Unit Assessment
2. Identify equivalent fractions (e.g., $\frac{3}{6} = \frac{1}{2}$ and $\frac{1}{3} = \frac{2}{6}$.)	**Sessions 2.2, 2.3, 2.4:** Fraction Cookie Game	**Sessions 2.3 and 2.4 Assessment Activity:** Many Ways to Make a Share  **Session 3.4 Assessment Activity:** End-of-Unit Assessment
3. Find combinations of fractions that are equal to one and to other fractions (e. g., $\frac{3}{6} + \frac{1}{2} = 1$; $\frac{1}{6} + \frac{1}{6} = \frac{1}{3}$; and $\frac{1}{3} + \frac{1}{6} = \frac{1}{2}$).	**Sessions 2.2, 2.3, 2.4:** Fraction Cookie Game	**Sessions 2.3 and 2.4 Assessment Activity:** Many Ways to Make a Share **Session 3.4 Assessment Activity:** End-of-Unit Assessment

☑ Checklist Available

Relating the Mathematical Emphases to the Benchmarks

Mathematical Emphases	Benchmarks
Rational Numbers Understanding the meaning of fractions (halves, fourths, eighths, thirds, sixths) and decimal fractions (0.50, 0.25) as equal parts of a whole (an object, an area, a set of objects)	1, 2
Rational Numbers Using representations to combine fractions (halves, fourths, eighths, thirds, and sixths)	3

The **Classroom Routines** and **Ten-Minute Math** activities, to be done in ten minutes outside of math class, are introduced in a unit and repeated throughout the grade. Specific directions for the day's activity are provided in each session. For the full description and variations of the Classroom Routines and Ten-Minute Math activities, see *Implementing Investigations in Grade 3*.

Activity	Introduced	Full Description of Activity and Its Variations
Classroom Routines: *What's the Temperature?*	Unit 1, Session 1.1	*Implementing Investigations in Grade 3*
Ten-Minute Math: *Today's Number*	Unit 2, Session 1.6	*Implementing Investigations in Grade 3*
Ten-Minute Math: *What Time Is It?*	Unit 3, Session 3.1	*Implementing Investigations in Grade 3*

What's the Temperature?

Students record the outside temperature every Wednesday morning on a chart and on a graph. They continue to practice reading charts and graphs, considering the relationship between them, and discussing changes in temperature over time.

Today's Number

Students write several different expressions that equal a given number up to 950 (or $9.50). They work with constraints that define the operations and the number relationships they can use, in order to practice and develop flexibility with computation skills.

Math Focus Points

◆ Generating equivalent expressions for a number using particular constraints

◆ Practicing computation skills

◆ Using notation to record expressions

What Time Is It?

Students practice naming, notating, telling, and setting time to the minute on analog and digital clocks. They predict ending times when given intervals and the starting times of activities, and determine the length of various amounts of time.

Math Focus Points

◆ Telling time to any minute on a digital or analog clock

◆ Determining intervals of time to the minute

Practice and Review

Practice and review play a critical role in the *Investigations* program. The following components and features are available to provide regular reinforcement of key mathematical concepts and procedures.

Books	Features	In This Unit ...
Curriculum Unit	**The Classroom Routines** and **Ten-Minute Math** activities, to be done in ten minutes outside of math class, are introduced in a unit and repeated throughout the grade. Specific directions for the day's activity are provided in each session. For the full description and variations of the Classroom Routines and Ten-Minute Math activities, see *Implementing Investigations in Grade 3*.	• **All sessions**
Student Activity Book	**Daily Practice** pages in the *Student Activity Book* provide one of three types of written practice: **reinforcement** of the content of the unit, **ongoing review,** or **enrichment** opportunities. Some Daily Practice pages will also have Ongoing Review items with multiple-choice problems similar to those on standardized tests.	• **All sessions**
	Homework pages in the *Student Activity Book* are an extension of the work done in class. At times they help students prepare for upcoming activities.	• **Session 1.2** • **Session 2.4** • **Session 1.4** • **Session 3.1** • **Session 1.5** • **Session 3.2** • **Session 2.2**
Student Math Handbook	**Math Words and Ideas** in the *Student Math Handbook* are pages that summarize key words and ideas. Most Words and Ideas pages have at least one exercise.	• **Student Math Handbook, pp. 56–65**
	Games pages are found in a section of the *Student Math Handbook*.	• **Student Math Handbook, pp. G11–G12**

Supporting the Range of Learners

The **Differentiation and Intervention Guide** provides Intervention, Extension, and Practice activities for use within each Investigation.

Sessions	1.1	1.2	1.3	1.4	1.5	2.1	2.2	2.3	2.4	3.2
Intervention	•	•			•			•	•	•
Extension	•	•	•	•	•	•		•	•	•
ELL	•			•			•		•	•

Intervention

Suggestions are made to support and engage students who are having difficulty with a particular idea, activity, or problem.

Extension

Suggestions are made to support and engage students who finish early or may be ready for additional challenge.

English Language Learners (ELL)

In this unit, students focus on the meaning of fractions and decimal fractions as equal parts of a whole. While English Language Learners may have developed facility with the names of whole numbers, making the transition to naming fractions can be challenging. For example, students will need practice in naming the 4 they see in the fraction $\frac{1}{4}$ as a *fourth* rather than *four*.

Make a chart of numerical fractions ($\frac{1}{2}$, $\frac{1}{3}$, $\frac{1}{4}$, etc.) and their corresponding names (one half, one third, one fourth/quarter, etc.) for English Language Learners to refer to throughout the unit. Ask students to identify the part of the fraction that says fourths, sixths, eighths, etc. Add decimal fractions and their corresponding names to the chart as you begin the work with decimals. Throughout the unit, as the students write fractions and decimals, ask them to say them orally.

Using a variety of contexts such as rectangles representing "brownies," pattern block "cookies," and groups of objects, students in this unit determine common fraction equivalencies. To develop understanding of the term *equivalent fractions,* connect the word *equivalent* to the word *equal* and ask how the terms are similar. Then ask English Language Learners to use their rectangle "brownies" or pattern block "cookies" to show you equivalent fractions. For example, Show me $\frac{1}{3}$ of a cookie. Can you show me a fraction that's *equivalent* to $\frac{1}{3}$? Show me $\frac{2}{3}$ of a cookie. Can you show me a fraction that's *equivalent* to $\frac{2}{3}$? How do you know these fractions are *equivalent?*

During activities, check in with English Language Learners frequently. This will help students develop their ability to express ideas in English and will give you the opportunity to model the language of fractions and decimals in the context of the concrete materials or representations used in the sessions.

Working with the Range of Learners: Classroom Cases is a set of episodes written by teachers that focuses on meeting the needs of the range of learners in the classroom. In the first section, *Setting up the Mathematical Community,* teachers write about how they create a supportive and productive learning environment in their classrooms. In the next section, *Accommodations for Learning,* teachers focus on specific modifications they make to meet the needs of some of their learners. In the last section, *Language and Representation,* teachers share how they help students use representations and develop language to investigate and express mathematical ideas. The questions at the end of each case provide a starting point for your own reflection or for discussion with colleagues. See *Implementing Investigations in Grade 3* for this set of episodes.

Mathematical Emphases

Rational Numbers Understanding the meaning of fractions (halves, fourths, eighths, thirds, sixths) and decimal fractions (0.50, 0.25) as equal parts of a whole (an object, an area, a set of objects)

Math Focus Points

◆ Finding equal parts of a whole and naming them with fractions

◆ Dividing an area into equal parts

◆ Naming fractional parts with unit fractions ($\frac{1}{2}, \frac{1}{3}, \frac{1}{4}$, etc.)

◆ Ordering unit fractions

◆ Demonstrating that different-shaped pieces that are the same fraction of the same area have equal areas

◆ Naming fractional parts with fractions that have numerators greater than 1 ($\frac{3}{4}, \frac{2}{3}, \frac{3}{6}$, etc.)

◆ Dividing a group into equal parts and naming the parts with fractions

◆ Identifying equivalent fractional parts

◆ Using fraction notation to record equivalencies (e.g., $\frac{3}{6} = \frac{1}{2}, \frac{1}{2} = \frac{2}{4}$)

◆ Using mixed numbers to represent quantities greater than 1

Rational Numbers Using representations to combine fractions (halves, fourths, eighths, thirds, and sixths)

Math Focus Points

◆ Using representations to combine fractions that sum to 1 (e.g., $\frac{1}{4} + \frac{3}{4} = 1, \frac{1}{3} + \frac{1}{3} + \frac{1}{3} = 1, \frac{1}{2} + \frac{1}{4} + \frac{1}{4} = 1$)

Sharing Brownies

SESSION 1.1 p. 24	Student Activity Book	Student Math Handbook	Professional Development: Read Ahead of Time	
Making Fair Shares Students divide rectangles into equal pieces. They discuss how to prove that each piece is equal and how to label an equal share as a fraction of the whole.	1–3	56, 57, 58–59	• **Teacher Note:** Why Are Fractions Difficult?: Developing Meaning for Fractions, p. 109 • **Part 4: Ten-Minute Math** in *Implementing Investigations in Grade 3:* Today's Number • **Part 4: Classroom Routines** in *Implementing Investigations in Grade 3:* What's the Temperature?	
SESSION 1.2 p. 29				
Making Fraction Sets Students make and label fraction sets consisting of pieces that represent common unit fractions ($\frac{1}{2}, \frac{1}{4}, \frac{1}{8}, \frac{1}{3}, \frac{1}{6}$) and use the sets to place these fractions in order by size. They consider whether two differently shaped sixths of the same whole are equal.	4–5	57, 58–59		
SESSION 1.3 p. 36				
More Than One Piece Students work with fractions that have a numerator larger than 1 and find different ways to combine fractions to make one whole.	7	58, 59		
SESSION 1.4 p. 43				
Sharing Many Things Students solve problems in which they find fractions of a group of 12 objects.	8–10	57, 60	• **Part 4: Ten-Minute Math** in *Implementing Investigations in Grade 3:* What Time Is It?	

Classroom Routines and Ten-Minute Math

See page 16 for an overview.

What's the Temperature?
- Mount thermometer outside the classroom window.
- Post the Date and Temperature chart and Temperature graph in the classroom.

Today's Number
- No materials needed

What Time Is It?
- Demonstration clock
- Student clocks

Materials to Gather	Materials to Prepare
• **Scissors** (1 per student) • **Glue sticks or tape** (1 per pair or per 4 students)	• **M6, Large Brownies** Make copies on colored paper. Choose 3 or 4 different colors. (2 per student) • **M7–M8, Family Letter** Make copies. (1 per student) • **Chart paper** Write the title "Unequal Thirds." Draw a rectangle divided into three sections that are NOT equal.
• **$8\frac{1}{2}''$ x 11″ sheets of colored paper** (5 of one color per pair) • **Scissors** (1 per student) • **Envelopes or resealable plastic bags** (1 per pair) • **Rulers** (as needed)	• **M9–M10, Family Letter** Make copies. (1 per student) • **Chart paper** Write the title "Directions for Making a Fraction Set" at the top. Then write the directions for making Fraction Sets as shown in the session. • **Teacher Fraction Set** Use 5 different sheets of paper. Cut each piece into halves, fourths, thirds, sixths, or eighths.
• **Students' Fraction Sets** (from Session 1.2) • **$8\frac{1}{2}''$ x 11″ paper** (5 pieces per pair plus 1 extra for demonstration) • **Scissors** (1 per pair)	• **Chart paper** Write the title "Fraction Facts." Label one section "Halves, Fourths, and Eighths" and another section "Halves, Thirds, and Sixths."
• **Connecting cubes**	

Sharing Brownies, *continued*

SESSION 1.5 p. 47	Student Activity Book	Student Math Handbook	Professional Development: Read Ahead of Time	
Sharing Several Brownies Students solve problems about people sharing brownies. They compare equivalent fractions and fraction expressions.	11–13	57, 61–62, 63	• **Dialogue Box:** Seven Brownies, Four People, p. 120	

SESSION 1.6 p. 53				
Assessment: Sharing Four Brownies Students solve problems about sharing groups of objects. An assessment focuses on finding equal shares that include fractional parts.	15–17	56, 57, 60, 61–62	• **Teacher Note:** Assessment: Sharing Four Brownies, p. 111	

Materials to Gather	Materials to Prepare
• **Chart paper** (optional) • **Scissors** (1 per student) • **Glue sticks or tape** (1 per pair or per 4 students)	• **M11, Small Brownies** Make copies. (3 per student plus extras) • **M12, Sharing Several Brownies** Make copies. (8 per student) • **Chart paper** On the paper or on the board, write the title, "Sharing Several Brownies" and these problems: How can 2 people share 3 brownies? How can 2 people share 5 brownies? How can 3 people share 4 brownies? How can 3 people share 5 brownies? How can 4 people share 2 brownies? How can 4 people share 3 brownies? How can 3 people share 2 brownies? How can 6 people share 4 brownies?
• **M11, Small Brownies** (from Session 1.5; as needed) • **Connecting cubes** (as needed)	• **M13, Assessment: Sharing Four Brownies** Make copies. (1 per student)

Making Fair Shares

Math Focus Points

◆ Finding equal parts of a whole and naming them with fractions

◆ Dividing an area into equal parts

◆ Naming fraction parts with unit fractions ($\frac{1}{2}$, $\frac{1}{3}$, $\frac{1}{4}$, etc.)

Vocabulary
fraction
denominator
numerator

Today's Plan		Materials
ACTIVITY **① One Brownie to Share**	45 MIN · INDIVIDUALS	• *Student Activity Book,* pp. 1–2 • M6* • Scissors; glue sticks or tape
DISCUSSION **② Equal Shares**	15 MIN · CLASS	• Chart: "Unequal Thirds"*
SESSION FOLLOW-UP **③ Daily Practice**		• *Student Activity Book,* p. 3 • *Student Math Handbook,* pp. 56, 57, 58–59 • M7–M8, Family Letter*

*See *Materials to Prepare,* p. 21.

Ten-Minute Math

Today's Number Students create expressions that equal 378. They must use one combination that adds up to 100 in each expression they create; for example, *25 + 75 + 200 + 78 = 378,* and *49 + 51 + 250 + 28 = 378.* Collect a few expressions to write on the board and ask students:

· Which numbers in your expression equal 100 when added together? Are you sure that the whole expression equals 378?

ACTIVITY

1 One Brownie to Share

45 MIN INDIVIDUALS

In this unit, students share brownies and objects among different numbers of people and determine the fraction that is each person's equal share.❶

Distribute the copies of Large Brownies (M6).

During the next few days, you are going to solve some problems about sharing brownies. For these activities you are going to pretend that these rectangles are brownies.

Students spend a few minutes cutting up their "brownies." They cut along the dotted lines of Large Brownies (M6) to make rectangular brownies. Ask students to exchange some of their rectangles with their neighbors so that each student has an array of different-colored "brownies." This will allow students to have different-colored "brownies" for each problem.

Hold up one brownie.

Suppose that this is a brownie and that two people want to share this brownie. Think about how you can cut the brownie so that two people can have equal shares. You are going to use only straight lines or straight cuts, as if you were cutting your brownies with a knife.

Allow students a minute or two to either cut apart or draw lines on one of the brownies to divide it in half.

Then bring students together to share a few examples. Students will probably come up with the following:❷

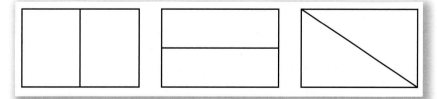

What would you call the share of the brownie that one person gets? What fraction of the brownie does each person get?

When students have identified $\frac{1}{2}$, write it on the board.

[Point to one half of the rectangle.] This piece is $\frac{1}{2}$ of the whole brownie. What does the number on the top stand for? What does the number on the bottom stand for?❸

Professional Development

❶ **Teacher Note:** Why Are Fractions Difficult?: Developing Meaning for Fractions, p. 109

Math Note

❷ **Different-Shaped Fractions** It may not be clear to third graders that the same-sized fraction of a whole can be shaped differently. If students make shares that are differently shaped (such as dividing the rectangle with a horizontal, vertical or diagonal line), ask them the same questions you would ask as they work on all their shares: "How do you know that these are equal? Does it matter which share you take?" Encourage students to use cutting and folding to prove equality.

❸ **Vocabulary** Mention that the top number is the *numerator* and the bottom number is the *denominator*. These are terms that students should hear throughout this unit, but they are not expected to use them until Grade 4. It is more important for students to understand the meaning of each in the context of these fair shares problems: the number on the bottom represents the total number of equal shares, and the top number identifies the number of those shares.

Teaching Note

④ Making Equal Shares Some students may have difficulty folding and cutting rectangles into equal parts. Thirds can be particularly difficult for third graders to fold accurately. Allow students time to work through this problem themselves and to help each other with the actual folding. If students are cutting their brownies quickly before they look to see if the pieces are equal, you might ask the student to fold their brownies first to show the shares or draw lines using a ruler. Students can always use other brownies to start a problem over again. Making fractional parts equal is a focus throughout this unit, and students will have several opportunities to make sure that fractional parts are the same size.

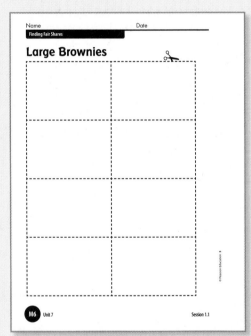

▲ Resource Masters, M6

Now you are going to share this one brownie among *more* than two people. Remember that each person gets an equal piece. Write the fraction name of each person's share. Check your work with a partner to see whether you each cut yours the same way or differently.

On *Student Activity Book* pages 1–2, students divide rectangular brownies, label them as fourths, eighths, thirds, and sixths, and paste them onto their papers.④

ONGOING ASSESSMENT: Observing Students at Work

Students divide rectangles into halves, fourths, eighths, thirds, and sixths.

- **Do students make equal pieces?**

- **Can students prove that their shares are equal by cutting, measuring, folding, or reasoning?** (Reasoning may include dividing halves in half to make fourths or knowing that a diagonal line divides a rectangle into two equal pieces.)

- **Can students label the shares with a fraction name?**

- **Do students use the way they divided brownies in previous problems to help them divide a brownie in a new problem (e.g., using a brownie divided into thirds and cutting each section in half to make sixths)?**

As students work, ask them to prove to you that all the shares are equal.

- Does it matter which piece you take? Are they all equal? How do you know? If 4 (8, 3, or 6) people shared this brownie and each got one of these pieces, would each person get a fair share? How do you know?

DIFFERENTIATION: Supporting the Range of Learners

Intervention If some students have difficulty creating equal shares and/or correctly labeling one share, remind them that each piece needs to be equal. Ask such questions as these: "Are these pieces equal? How do you know? If there are two equal pieces, how do we label one piece? It is one of two equal pieces, so it is called $\frac{1}{2}$. What about one of three equal pieces?" Students work on identifying and labeling fractions throughout this unit.

Extension Some students may easily finish the five problems on *Student Activity Book* pages 1–2. Help them extend the work they have done with one brownie by posing the following problems and questions:

- Suppose that 9 [12, 16] people were going to share one brownie. Think about how you divided a brownie in one of the problems you already did. How could that method help you make shares for 9 [12, 16] people? What fraction would one share be?

- If only two people ate their shares in Problem 2 [3, 4, 5], what fraction of the brownie would be left? (Students may provide a variety of correct responses; for instance, they may correctly answer this for Problem 2 by saying $\frac{1}{4} + \frac{1}{4}$, $\frac{2}{4}$, or $\frac{1}{2}$.)

ELL Work with English Language Learners for a few minutes before starting the activity to make sure they understand the basic vocabulary. Some students may not be familiar with brownies as a food item. Explain that a brownie is a kind of chocolate cake. Show students a brownie or a picture of a brownie if possible. Tell them they will be using paper and pretending the paper is brownies. Next write the word *share* on the board and have students repeat it. Say: When you share, you give part of something you have to someone else. Each part is also called a *share*. Demonstrate by sharing some crayons with one student. Say: I share my crayons with Alicia. This is my share, and this is her share. A "fair share" means we each get the same amount. Have partners demonstrate sharing items and repeat the sentences: I share my _____ with _____. This is my share, and this is her/his share. We each get a fair share.

DISCUSSION

2 Equal Shares

15 MIN CLASS

Math Focus Points for Discussion

◆ Finding equal parts of a whole and naming them with fractions

Display the chart "Unequal Thirds" on the board.

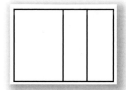

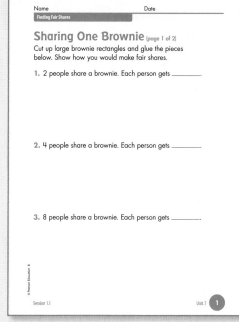

Sharing One Brownie (page 1 of 2)

Cut up large brownie rectangles and glue the pieces below. Show how you would make fair shares.

1. 2 people share a brownie. Each person gets _____.

2. 4 people share a brownie. Each person gets _____.

3. 8 people share a brownie. Each person gets _____.

▲ Student Activity Book, p. 1

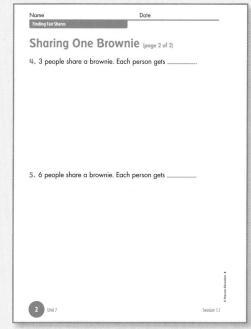

Sharing One Brownie (page 2 of 2)

4. 3 people share a brownie. Each person gets _____.

5. 6 people share a brownie. Each person gets _____.

▲ Student Activity Book, p. 2

▲ **Student Activity Book, p. 3**

Here is a brownie that has been cut up to share among three people. Would each person get an equal share? How would you prove that the shares are equal or not equal?

Students may suggest folding the brownie in half, observing that the first share is as big as the other two shares. Students may also suggest cutting out the three shares and putting them on top of one another to show that they are not equal. Allow students to demonstrate their suggestions for proving that the shares are not equal. Some students may say that they do not look equal. Acknowledge that this is true, but that it might not always be easy to tell by "just looking" and you would like them to think of a number of different ways to prove their idea.

Did anyone come up with a method for sharing a brownie equally among three people?

Have a number of brownies available for students to show how they made three equal shares. After each demonstration, ask these questions:

Are these shares equal? How could you prove that the shares are equal?

Finish the discussion by asking students for the fraction name for one share of a brownie shared equally among three people.

What fraction of a brownie would each person get if one brownie were shared among three people? How would you write one third? What does the bottom number (the denominator) stand for? What does the top number (the numerator) stand for?

SESSION FOLLOW-UP
③ Daily Practice

 Daily Practice: For ongoing review, have students complete *Student Activity Book* page 3.

 Student Math Handbook: Students and families may use *Student Math Handbook* pages 56, 57, 58–59 for reference and review. See pages 124–127 in the back of this unit.

 Family Letter: Send home copies of the Family Letter (M7–M8).

Making Fraction Sets

Math Focus Points

◆ Dividing an area into equal parts

◆ Ordering unit fractions

◆ Demonstrating that different-shaped pieces that are the same
fraction of the same area have equal areas

Today's Plan		Materials
ACTIVITY **①** **Making Fraction Sets**	🕐 25 MIN 👥 PAIRS	• Chart: "Directions for Making a Fraction Set"*; $8\frac{1}{2}$″ x 11″ sheets of colored paper; scissors; envelopes or resealable plastic bags; rulers
ACTIVITY **②** **From Smallest to Largest**	🕐 10 MIN 👥 CLASS 👥 PAIRS	• Teacher Fraction Set*
DISCUSSION **③** **Different Sizes, Different Shapes**	🕐 25 MIN 👥 CLASS 👥 PAIRS	• Teacher Fraction Set; Students' Fraction Sets (from Activity 2); scissors (optional)
SESSION FOLLOW-UP **④** **Daily Practice and Homework**		• *Student Activity Book,* pp. 4–5 • *Student Math Handbook,* pp. 57, 58–59 • M9–M10, Family Letter*

*See *Materials to Prepare,* p. 21.

Ten-Minute Math

Today's Number Students use only coin values (nickels, dimes, and quarters) and
dollars to create expressions using *addition and multiplication* that equal $5.00. Show
students how to use parentheses to show multiples of coin values in their expressions.
For example: $3.00 + (4 × $0.25) + (10 × $0.10) = $5.00. Collect a few expressions
to write on the board and ask students:

• How do you know your expression equals $5.00? How did you decide how to combine
these coin values?

Teaching Note

❶ **Writing Fractions** To make it easier to recognize "top" and "bottom" numbers, write all fractions that students will see with the numerator directly above the denominator and with the divide line horizontal rather than diagonal. For example, $\frac{2}{3}$ and $\frac{1}{6}$.

ACTIVITY

25 MIN   PAIRS

1 Making Fraction Sets

Give each pair of students five sheets of the same color $8\frac{1}{2}''$ x 11″ paper. Explain that they will be using these sheets to make Fraction Sets. Then demonstrate the process: fold a piece of paper in half, mark the fold line with a pencil, unfold it, and show it to your students.

How many equal pieces did I make? What fraction is each part? How do you write that?

Write $\frac{1}{2}$ on each section in pencil and $\frac{1}{2}$ on the board.❶

I gave you five sheets of paper. You and your partner are going to fold and cut one sheet of paper into two equal pieces, one sheet into four equal pieces, one sheet into eight equal pieces, one sheet into three equal pieces, and one sheet into six equal pieces.

Then you will label each piece with its fraction name, as I did on my halves. I wrote $\frac{1}{2}$ on each piece.

Post the directions that you prepared on chart paper.

Directions for Making a Fraction Set

1. You should have 5 sheets of the same color paper.

2. Cut each sheet of paper into equal pieces.

   a. 1st sheet—2 equal pieces

   b. 2nd sheet—4 equal pieces

   c. 3rd sheet—8 equal pieces

   d. 4th sheet—3 equal pieces

   e. 5th sheet—6 equal pieces

3. Fold the first sheet of paper into equal pieces and draw lines to separate them.

4. Label each piece with the fraction name.

5. Check with another pair to make sure that you have equal pieces and that your fraction name is correct.

6. Cut apart each equal piece.

7. Repeat steps 3–6 with each sheet until you have a complete Fraction Set.

After you have labeled your pieces on each sheet, compare your pieces with another pair. Do you agree that you have equal pieces and that your fraction names are correct? If you do, then cut your pieces apart.

Hold up your sheet of halves.

So I'm going to double-check: Did I make equal pieces? Are these each $\frac{1}{2}$ of the whole paper? Are these the correct fraction names?

Then cut your halves apart. Students work in pairs to do the same with their five sheets of paper, creating a Fraction Set of halves, fourths, eighths, thirds, and sixths.

Students may cut their fractions in different ways. For example, some may be horizontal and some vertical. At the end of the session, students will compare two differently shaped sixths and discuss whether they are equal, even though they look different. As students make their Fraction Sets, look for examples of these two shapes of sixths, and ask students who have made these to be prepared to share them in the discussion.

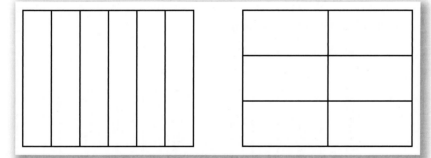

Distribute envelopes or resealable plastic bags to hold each Fraction Set. Students use these sets as a visual reference throughout the unit as they continue to solve problems with fractions.

ONGOING ASSESSMENT: Observing Students at Work

Students divide letter-sized paper into equal parts to create Fraction Sets of pieces that are $\frac{1}{2}$, $\frac{1}{4}$, $\frac{1}{8}$, $\frac{1}{3}$, and $\frac{1}{6}$ of the whole sheet.

- **Do students create pieces that are the same size?**

- **Can students correctly label their pieces?**

As students work, ask pairs about how they are dividing up their pieces of paper. As with the brownies, ask students to show that the pieces they have made by folding are equal. Also ask students what the fraction names of the pieces are and how they know.

DIFFERENTIATION: Supporting the Range of Learners

Intervention Some students may have trouble figuring out how to fold the paper to make equal pieces. Remind them of the last activity of sharing brownies, and ask them how the work they did in that activity could help them. Encourage students to talk with their partners and come to an agreement about whether their pieces are equal, whether they have enough pieces, and whether they have labeled their pieces correctly.

ACTIVITY

10 MIN   CLASS   PAIRS

2 From Smallest to Largest

When most students have almost finished making their Fraction Sets, bring the class together briefly to give them instructions for the next activity with the Fraction Sets: placing one of each size fraction in order from smallest to largest. Show students the Fraction Set you made, taped in random order to the board.

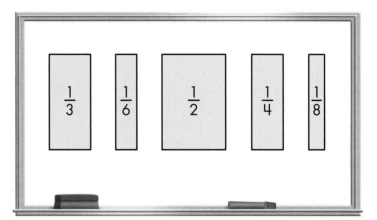

I want to order these fraction pieces from smallest to largest, with the smallest over here (to the left) and the largest over here (to the right). Which of these would be the smallest?

Although many students will claim that the $\frac{1}{8}$ piece is the smallest, some students may not be sure. Sometimes the difference between sixths and eighths is difficult to see without a close inspection. Give students a minute to discuss this as a class, and then let them know that they should continue this discussion with their partners. Students then order their own Fraction Sets from smallest to largest. They will discuss their ordering at the end of the session.

ONGOING ASSESSMENT: Observing Students at Work

Students order the pieces that represent the unit fractions $\frac{1}{2}, \frac{1}{4}, \frac{1}{8}, \frac{1}{3}$, and $\frac{1}{6}$ from smallest to largest.

- **Do students judge the size of each fraction by measuring one against the other in some way?** Can they order these fractions accurately?

- **Do some students use the denominator to determine the size of the fraction?** Do they notice anything about the relationship between the size of the denominator and the size of the piece?

DIFFERENTIATION: Supporting the Range of Learners

Extension As some students finish making their sets and others are still finishing, ask the students who have finished to use their sets to see what they can find out about some relationships among the fractions they created.

- Are there any fractional pieces you can combine to make other fractional pieces or to make a whole?

The whole class will work on this activity during the next session.

DISCUSSION

25 MIN   CLASS   PAIRS

Different Sizes, Different Shapes

Math Focus Points for Discussion

- Ordering unit fractions
- Demonstrating that different-shaped pieces that are the same fraction of the same area have equal areas

Bring the class together to look again at the Fraction Set pieces you taped to the board. If there is disagreement about the correct order, ask students to share their reasoning.

What did you and your partner notice about the order of these fractions as you compared them?

As students share, allow them to go to the board as needed to compare physically the fractional pieces.

Math Note

❷ **The Smaller the Denominator, the Larger the Unit Fraction** Some students notice something important about unit fractions ($\frac{1}{2}$, $\frac{1}{3}$, $\frac{1}{4}$, and so on) as they divide identical wholes into halves, fourths, eighths, thirds, and sixths and learn fractional notation to represent each piece. They notice that as the denominator of these unit fractions gets larger, the corresponding fractional piece gets smaller. When using whole numbers, students know that 3 is greater than 2 and 4 is greater than 3. Why is something with a 4 in the notation now *smaller* than something with a 3 in the notation? At this point in the unit, many students will be engaged with this question. As the unit continues, encourage students to talk about their observations about fraction notation and the meaning of these observations. For instance, they should think through what $\frac{1}{4}$ represents and how it compares with a fraction with a smaller denominator, such as $\frac{1}{3}$. Leave the ordered Fraction Set displayed so that students have a visual reference for this idea.

Students may make a variety of observations about the fractions as they compare them. Some observations that represent important ideas about fractions include the following:

- Some of the fractions are hard to compare, such as $\frac{1}{8}$ and $\frac{1}{6}$. They are close in size and students need to compare them physically by cutting, folding, or placing one on top of the other. Simply looking at each separately may not provide enough information.

- A few students may notice that the smallest fraction has the largest denominator. If students notice this, ask them why this is true.❷

- Some equivalent fractions may have been cut out into different shapes. For example, some students may have cut "thin" sixths, and some may have cut "chunky" sixths. These are equal, but they look different.

If this has not come up in students' work, bring it up yourself by drawing two ways to make fourths or sixths. Ask students to consider whether both shapes are sixths (or fourths) of the whole sheet.

Could both of these shapes be sixths? How can you find out whether they're the same size? Talk to your partner about this. There are blank pieces of paper here if you want to make the other sixth that's different from your own so that you can compare them.

Some students will manipulate the pieces in some way to make them "match." For example, one student cut a sixth "strip" into halves and covered the "chunky" sixths.

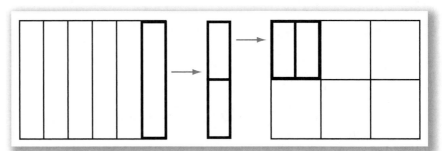

Some students may be able to reason that as long as the whole started out the same size, the sixths have to be equal in area because the same amount of area was divided into six equal parts.

SESSION FOLLOW-UP

Daily Practice and Homework

 Daily Practice: For ongoing review, have students complete *Student Activity Book* page 4.

 Homework: On *Student Activity Book* page 5, students divide different shapes in half.

 Student Math Handbook: Students and families may use *Student Math Handbook* pages 57, 58–59 for reference and review. See pages 124–127 in the back of this unit.

 Family Letter: Send home copies of the Family Letter (M9–M10).

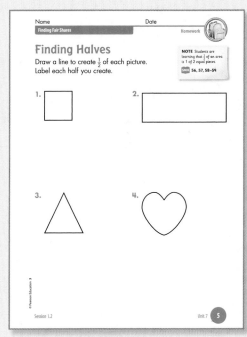

▲ **Student Activity Book, p. 4**

▲ **Student Activity Book, p. 5**

More Than One Piece

Math Focus Points

- Naming fractional parts with fractions that have numerators greater than 1 ($\frac{3}{4}, \frac{2}{3}, \frac{3}{6}$, etc.)

- Using representations to combine fractions that sum to 1 (e.g., $\frac{1}{4} + \frac{3}{4} = 1, \frac{1}{3} + \frac{1}{3} + \frac{1}{3} = 1, \frac{1}{2} + \frac{1}{4} + \frac{1}{4} = 1$)

Today's Plan		Materials
ACTIVITY ❶ **More Than One Piece**	25 MIN · PAIRS	• Blank 8 $\frac{1}{2}$″ x 11″ paper; scissors
ACTIVITY ❷ **Many Ways to Make a Whole**	20 MIN · PAIRS · CLASS	• Chart: "Fraction Facts"*; Students' Fraction Sets (from Session 1.2); "More Than One Piece" fractions (from Activity 1)
DISCUSSION ❸ **Fraction Facts**	15 MIN · CLASS	• Chart: "Fraction Facts" (from Activity 2)
SESSION FOLLOW-UP ❹ **Daily Practice**		• *Student Activity Book*, p. 7 • *Student Math Handbook*, pp. 58, 59

*See *Materials to Prepare,* p. 21.

Ten-Minute Math

Today's Number Students create expressions that equal 419 using addition. They must use multiples of 10 in each expression they create. For example: $419 = 300 + 50 + 60 + 9$, and $80 + 20 + 319 = 419$. Collect a few expressions to write on the board and ask students:

- How do you know this expression equals 419? How did you combine the multiples of 10?

ACTIVITY

1 More Than One Piece

Explain to students that they will be folding paper to create different fractions. They begin to identify fractions with numerators greater than one.

Fold an $8\frac{1}{2}''$ x $11''$ piece of paper into fourths.

What fraction is each of the pieces on this paper I have folded?

After the class has determined that the pieces are fourths, cut a $\frac{1}{4}$ piece out of the paper.

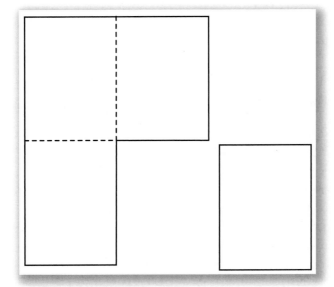

What fraction did I cut out of the paper?

Label the piece cut out $\frac{1}{4}$. Then ask students to look at what is left.

How much do I have left?

Some students may say "one fourth and (or plus) one fourth and one fourth," and some may say "three fourths." If no one uses the term "three fourths," ask them to consider how they would combine all of the remaining fourths.

One fourth plus one fourth plus one fourth is one way to name what is left. Can anyone think of another fraction name for what is left? If the pieces are all fourths, and this part here is three of them instead of just one, how would I write that?

Some students may know how to notate three fourths. If not, show how to write $\frac{3}{4}$ on the board and then on the paper.

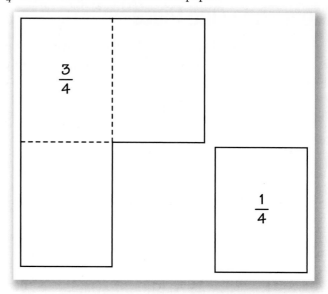

Hand out five sheets of blank paper to each pair of students.

Now, with your partner, you are going to add more pieces to your Fraction Set. These pieces will show fractions that have more than one piece. You will need to make one sheet of *halves,* one sheet of *fourths,* one sheet of *eighths,* one sheet of *thirds,* and one sheet of *sixths.* After you have folded the paper into the fractional parts, you are NOT going to cut out all the pieces as you did the last time. Instead, you are going to cut out only one piece as I just did for the fourths. For each sheet you make, you will label the piece you cut out and also the piece that is left.

ONGOING ASSESSMENT: Observing Students at Work

Students create and label pieces of a whole that represent fractional parts with numerators greater than one.

- **Can students fold the whole piece of paper into equal pieces for each fraction?**

- **Can students correctly label both unit fractions and fractions with numerators greater than one?**

- **Can students produce pieces that represent all of the following: $\frac{1}{2}, \frac{1}{4}, \frac{3}{4}, \frac{1}{8}, \frac{7}{8}, \frac{1}{3}, \frac{2}{3}, \frac{1}{6},$ and $\frac{5}{6}$?**

DIFFERENTIATION: Supporting the Range of Learners

Extension If some students quickly finish making their fraction sets, ask them to work on putting all the fractions in order (the cut-out pieces and the leftover pieces). Some of these fractions are difficult to place in order (e.g., $\frac{2}{3}$ and $\frac{3}{4}$ or $\frac{5}{6}$ and $\frac{7}{8}$). Encourage students to use the Fraction Set pieces they made to compare size and to also think about how the sizes of these pieces relate to the whole and to the fractional part. For example, some students may reason that $\frac{7}{8}$ has to be bigger than $\frac{3}{4}$ because the $\frac{1}{8}$ piece that is missing from the former is smaller than the $\frac{1}{4}$ piece that is missing from the latter.

ACTIVITY

20 MIN   PAIRS   CLASS

② Many Ways to Make a Whole

Bring the class together, and show students the Fraction Facts chart that you prepared. Students will need their Fraction Sets.

As we keep working with fractions, we're going to use this chart to help us keep track of things we notice or discover that are true about fractions. Let's start with what we can find out from the Fraction Sets you've been making.

Show students the $\frac{1}{4}$ and $\frac{3}{4}$ pieces that you made at the beginning of the session.

If I combine these two fractions, what will I have? [a whole] How could I write an equation that says that one fourth and three fourths make a whole?

Following students' suggestions, on the section of the Fraction Facts chart titled "Halves, Fourths, and Eighths," write $\frac{1}{4} + \frac{3}{4} = 1$.

What other ways can you think of to make a whole with fractions? With your partner, use your Fraction Sets to find different ways to make a whole.

Students may keep track of their findings on blank paper. You will be collecting their ideas to record on the class chart later in the session.

Students use their Fraction Sets to find different ways to make a whole.

ONGOING ASSESSMENT: Observing Students at Work

Students combine pieces representing fractional parts to make a whole.

- **Can students combine both like and unlike fractions to make a whole?** Do they use reasoning as well as the physical combination of fraction pieces (e.g., "I know that two fourths make a half, so I can put that with another half, even though our pieces don't fit so well because of how we cut them")?

As students are working, encourage them to look for many different ways to combine their pieces. They can combine unit fractions and "more than one piece" fractions (e.g., $\frac{1}{4} + \frac{3}{4}$), multiple copies of the same fractional parts (e.g., $\frac{1}{3} + \frac{1}{3} + \frac{1}{3}$), or different unit fractions (e.g., $\frac{1}{2} + \frac{1}{4} + \frac{1}{4}$).

If students have combined fractions in only one way (such as $\frac{1}{3} + \frac{1}{3} + \frac{1}{3}$ or $\frac{1}{4} + \frac{1}{4} + \frac{1}{4} + \frac{1}{4}$) and seem stuck or think they are finished, start a new combination for them and ask them to finish it (e.g., $\frac{1}{2} + \frac{1}{4}$).

DISCUSSION

③ Fraction Facts

15 MIN CLASS

Math Focus Points for Discussion

◆ Using representations to combine fractions that sum to 1
(e.g., $\frac{1}{4} + \frac{3}{4} = 1$, $\frac{1}{3} + \frac{1}{3} + \frac{1}{3} = 1$, $\frac{1}{2} + \frac{1}{4} + \frac{1}{4} = 1$)

Bring the class together to share the combinations they found that make a whole. As students share, ask them to show their combinations with their fraction pieces, and record their solutions on the Fraction Facts chart under the appropriate heading (e.g., $\frac{1}{3} + \frac{1}{3} + \frac{1}{3} = 1$ goes in the section titled "Halves, Thirds, and Sixths," and $\frac{1}{2} + \frac{2}{4} = 1$ goes in the section titled "Halves, Fourths, and Eighths"). Some students may have a clear idea how to write equations that show the relationships they discovered. Others can show what they discovered with their Fraction Sets and you, or another student, can record their findings on the chart.

In order to record one student's solution on the chart, another student writes an equation that represents the diagram.

Write students' discoveries in a variety of ways on the chart. Write some of the students' suggestions in words; for example, "six sixths are one whole." Be sure to record combinations of same-size fractional pieces as equations with both unit fractions and with numerators larger than one. For example, four fourths equaling one whole can be written as $\frac{1}{4} + \frac{1}{4} + \frac{1}{4} + \frac{1}{4} = 1$ or as $\frac{4}{4} = 1$.

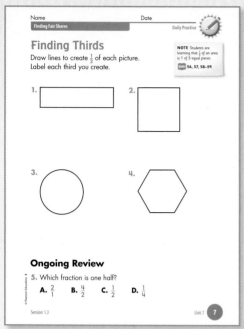

▲ Student Activity Book, p. 7

Keep these lists posted throughout the unit. Students will add to the lists in future sessions as they discover new relationships among fractions. At this point, a chart may appear as follows:

Fraction Facts

Halves, Fourths, and Eighths	Halves, Thirds, and Sixths
$\frac{1}{4} + \frac{3}{4} = 1$	$\frac{1}{3} + \frac{1}{3} + \frac{1}{3} = 1$
$\frac{1}{2} + \frac{2}{4} = 1$	Six sixths are one whole.
$\frac{1}{4} + \frac{1}{4} + \frac{1}{4} + \frac{1}{4} = 1$	
$\frac{4}{4} = 1$	

SESSION FOLLOW-UP
4 Daily Practice

 Daily Practice: For reinforcement of this unit's content, have students complete *Student Activity Book* page 7.

Student Math Handbook: Students and families may use *Student Math Handbook* pages 58, 59 for reference and review. See pages 124–127 in the back of this unit.

Sharing Many Things

Math Focus Points

◆ Dividing a group into equal parts and naming the parts with fractions

Today's Plan	Materials
ACTIVITY **①** Introducing Fractions of 12 🕐 15 MIN 👥 CLASS 👤 INDIVIDUALS	
ACTIVITY **②** Fractions of 12 🕐 30 MIN 👤 INDIVIDUALS	• *Student Activity Book,* p. 8 • Connecting cubes
DISCUSSION **③** Equal Shares 🕐 15 MIN 👥 CLASS	
SESSION FOLLOW-UP **④** Daily Practice and Homework	• *Student Activity,* pp. 9–10 • *Student Math Handbook,* pp. 57, 60

Ten-Minute Math

What Time Is It? Show 1:06 on the demonstration clock. Ask students:

• What time is it on this clock? If I start jogging at 1:06 and return 40 minutes later, what time will it be?

In pairs, students share ideas about what time they think it will be. Collect strategies based on numerical reasoning such as: "I know that $6 + 40 = 46$ so it would be 1:46." Ask students a similar question, starting with 3:39 as the starting time and 26 minutes for duration.

Math Note

❶ Fractions of a Set of Objects Fractions can represent many kinds of situations. The two that students work with in this unit are fractions of a single item, such as a brownie, and fractions of a group, such as the class. As adults, we may no longer see the use of fractions in these two kinds of situations as different. However, for students, dividing a single whole into fourths seems quite different from dividing a group of 12 people into fourths. First, the action is different: to divide a brownie into fourths, students typically fold or draw lines; to divide a group of 12 people into fourths, students might move counters—representing the people—into four groups. Second, the arithmetic of dividing a single entity looks different to students than the arithmetic involved in dividing a group. If a brownie is divided into fourths, each part is $\frac{1}{4}$ of the brownie. If the people are divided in fourths, each of the groups is also $\frac{1}{4}$ of the people and there are 3 people in each group ($\frac{1}{4}$ of 12 = 3). Figuring out how "$\frac{1}{4}$ of 12" relates to the quantity 3 is a new part of students' work that does not come up when they are considering fractions of single objects. It is important that students develop visual images both for parts of one whole and for parts of a group of things and learn to relate fractions to these parts in both kinds of situations.

ACTIVITY

15 MIN CLASS INDIVIDUALS

① Introducing Fractions of 12

In the previous sessions, students worked with an area model for fractions, finding parts of a single whole. In this session, they find fractions of groups of objects.❶

We have been finding fractions of rectangles, which are single objects that can be cut up into equal parts. It is also possible to find fractions of a group of things. Think about this: I have 12 marbles in my collection. I want to give my friend half of them. How many marbles will I give to my friend?

Allow students to consider this for a minute or two, and then ask a few students to explain how they thought about the question. As students share, encourage them to draw a picture that represents the problem on the board and to use their pictures to explain and justify their answers.

Students might say:

"I drew 12 circles—one for each marble—in a line. I drew a line across the middle of the marbles so that there was the same number of marbles on each side. I counted the marbles on one side and it is 6. So you gave her 6 marbles."

Sample Student Work

"I know that 6 + 6 = 12. So half of 12 is 6."

"I started putting out 12 cubes, but when I counted out 6 I realized that half of 12 things is 6 things because 6 fits into 12 evenly twice."

ACTIVITY

2 Fractions of 12

30 MIN INDIVIDUALS

Today you will be solving some problems about sharing 12 apples. Think about how you can picture these problems. You may want to use cubes, drawings, or any other materials that you think might be useful. Share your answers with a neighbor and compare your work.

Students solve problems about sharing 12 things equally on *Student Activity Book* page 8.

ONGOING ASSESSMENT: Observing Students at Work

Students find fractions of sets of discrete objects.

- **Can students find and name fractional parts of 12 objects?**

- **Can students use pictures or models to show that they have identified the correct fraction (e.g., rectangles or cubes)?**

DIFFERENTIATION: Supporting the Range of Learners

Extension If some students finish early, encourage them to draw pictures for each of the problems to represent each fraction. You may want students to share some of these in the discussion that follows.

ELL Before beginning the activity, review key vocabulary terms, such as *groups* for English Language Learners. Review also the structure of fractions and the conventions for reading fractions in English. Students from other cultures may have learned to read fractions in a different way.

DISCUSSION

3 Equal Shares

15 MIN CLASS

Math Focus Points for Discussion

◆ Dividing a group into equal parts and naming the parts with fractions

You found many fractions of 12 when you solved the problems about apples. Let's record what you found. What's $\frac{1}{2}$ of 12? What other fractions did you find?

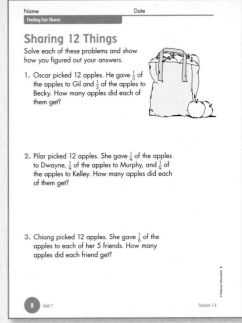

Name _____ Date _____

Finding Fair Shares

Sharing 12 Things

Solve each of these problems and show how you figured out your answers.

1. Oscar picked 12 apples. He gave $\frac{1}{3}$ of the apples to Gil and $\frac{1}{3}$ of the apples to Becky. How many apples did each of them get?

2. Pilar picked 12 apples. She gave $\frac{1}{4}$ of the apples to Dwayne, $\frac{1}{4}$ of the apples to Murphy, and $\frac{1}{4}$ of the apples to Kelley. How many apples did each of them get?

3. Chiang picked 12 apples. She gave $\frac{1}{6}$ of the apples to each of her 5 friends. How many apples did each friend get?

8 Unit 7   Session 1.4

▲ **Student Activity Book, p. 8**

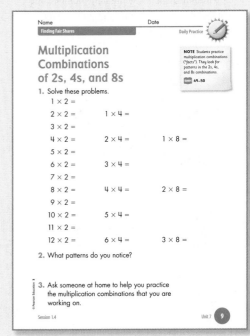

Name _____ Date _____

Finding Fair Shares   Daily Practice

Multiplication Combinations of 2s, 4s, and 8s

NOTE Students practice multiplication combinations ("facts"). They look for patterns in the 2s, 4s, and 8s combinations. *Skills* 49–50

1. Solve these problems.

$1 \times 2 =$
$2 \times 2 =$ $1 \times 4 =$
$3 \times 2 =$
$4 \times 2 =$ $2 \times 4 =$ $1 \times 8 =$
$5 \times 2 =$
$6 \times 2 =$ $3 \times 4 =$
$7 \times 2 =$
$8 \times 2 =$ $4 \times 4 =$ $2 \times 8 =$
$9 \times 2 =$
$10 \times 2 =$ $5 \times 4 =$
$11 \times 2 =$
$12 \times 2 =$ $6 \times 4 =$ $3 \times 8 =$

2. What patterns do you notice?

3. Ask someone at home to help you practice the multiplication combinations that you are working on.

Session 1.4   Unit 7 9

▲ **Student Activity Book, p. 9**

Math Note

❷ Half of the Class Because some classes have an even number of students and some have an odd number of students, the answer may or may not include a fraction. It is important to note that the exact answer for $\frac{1}{2}$ of 25 is $12\frac{1}{2}$, and students should be able to show how they know that each half is equal. Practically, in a situation such as dividing the class into two groups, the groups will have to be uneven (12 in one and 13 in the other) because you cannot really divide a person in half. A student who claims, "You can't divide our class in half because it's an odd number," is correct in terms of real actions. However, dividing in half mathematically can still be imagined. In fact, the student who says, "You can't do it because you can't have $12\frac{1}{2}$ people" actually understands the mathematics of dividing 25 in half. Pose another problem if there are students who need another example in order to visualize dividing an odd number in half. Use the same number, but choose objects that can be physically divided, such as slices of bread.

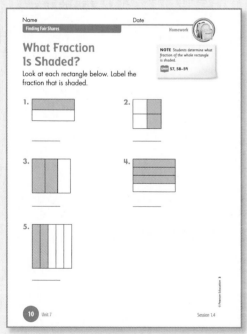

▲ Student Activity Book, p. 10

Write each fraction on the board as students say it: "$\frac{1}{2}$ of 12 is 6, $\frac{1}{3}$ of 12 is 4, $\frac{1}{4}$ of 12 is 3, and $\frac{1}{6}$ of 12 is 2."

Let's look together at $\frac{1}{6}$ of 12. How do you know that $\frac{1}{6}$ of 12 is 2? How many equal groups of apples do you have to make? How can you show me?

Encourage students to use pictures of objects as they explain their thinking. Many students will show 12 objects and portion them out into six groups with two objects in each group. They will see that one portion ($\frac{1}{6}$) is two objects.

Some students may reason that six fits into 12 two times, so each group has two apples (i.e., $12 \div 6 = 2$).

What about finding a fraction of a different number? How many students is $\frac{1}{2}$ of our class?

Allow students a few minutes to work on this with a partner. Encourage students to take out cubes, draw pictures, use a class list, or use any other material that might be useful to them. Then collect responses.❷

Collect a few examples of how students divided the class in half, and record the answer on the board. If you have time, pose a problem with a different number of students, for example: "If one person were absent tomorrow and we wanted to divide the class in half, how many would be in each half? What if two people were absent?"

SESSION FOLLOW-UP

 4 Daily Practice and Homework

 Daily Practice: For ongoing review, have students complete *Student Activity Book* page 9.

 Homework: On *Student Activity Book* page 10, students solve problems in which they name fractional parts of rectangles.

Student Math Handbook: Students and families may use *Student Math Handbook* pages 57, 60 for reference and review. See pages 124–127 in the back of this unit.

Sharing Several Brownies

Math Focus Points

◆ Dividing a group into equal parts and naming the parts with fractions

◆ Identifying equivalent fractional parts

◆ Using fraction notation to record equivalencies (e.g., $\frac{3}{6} = \frac{1}{2}$, $\frac{1}{2} = \frac{2}{4}$)

◆ Using mixed numbers to represent quantities greater than 1

Vocabulary

equivalent fractions

Today's Plan		Materials
ACTIVITY **①** **Sharing Seven Brownies**	20 MIN CLASS	• *Student Activity Book,* p. 11 • M11*
DISCUSSION **②** **Are These Shares Equal?**	20 MIN PAIRS	
ACTIVITY **③** **Sharing Several Brownies**	20 MIN INDIVIDUALS	• M12* • Chart: "Sharing Several Brownies"*; chart paper (optional) • scissors; glue sticks or tape
SESSION FOLLOW-UP **④** **Daily Practice and Homework**		• *Student Activity Book,* pp. 12–13 • *Student Math Handbook,* pp. 57, 61–62, 63

*See *Materials to Prepare,* p. 23.

Ten-Minute Math

What Time Is It? Write 8:43 on the board and ask students to show the time on their clocks. Then tell students:

• If I start practicing piano at 8:43 and I practice for 50 minutes, what time will it be when I finish?

In pairs, students share ideas about what time they think it will be and show the new time on their clocks. As a class, make sure students can "cross over" the hour. Focus on counting by 10s. Ask students a similar question, starting with 4:31 as the starting time and 42 minutes for duration.

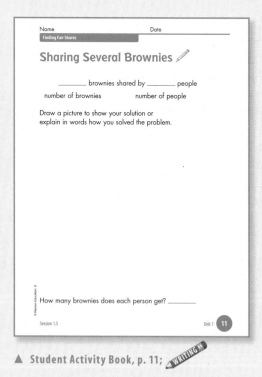

▲ Resource Masters, M11

Name _____ Date _____
Finding Fair Shares

Sharing Several Brownies

_____ brownies shared by _____ people
number of brownies   number of people

Draw a picture to show your solution or
explain in words how you solved the problem.

How many brownies does each person get? _____

Session 1.5   Unit 7 **11**

▲ Student Activity Book, p. 11; *WRITING*

ACTIVITY

20 MIN   CLASS

1 Sharing Seven Brownies

Introduce the following problem to the class by drawing seven rectangles on a "plate" and four faces.

Imagine that there are seven brownies to share equally among four people. About how many brownies do you think each person will get? Do you think each person will get one brownie? Two brownies? More than two brownies?

Ask two or three students to share their estimates and their reasoning.

Work with a partner to find out exactly how many brownies each person will get.

Students use small brownies on Small Brownies (M11), to cut out brownie rectangles as needed for each activity during this and the next session. Mention that these brownies are smaller than the ones students worked with in Session 1.1. Students use *Student Activity Book* page 11 to record their work on this problem.

Before starting, students fill in the blanks at the top of the page for the problem you have presented: seven brownies shared by four people.

Use the paper brownies to help you figure out the solution. Even though you are working in pairs, each of you should show clearly on your own paper how much brownie each person will get. You can glue the brownies or pieces of brownies on the paper to help show your solution. You may want to also draw quick pictures to help illustrate how much brownie each person gets. You need to label the shares with fractions to show how much each person gets.

Students typically approach this problem in two different ways. Some students start by giving out whole brownies to each person. Others divide each brownie into fourths because there are four people sharing and distribute the fourths until they are gone.❶

Professional Development

❶ **Dialogue Box:** Seven Brownies, Four People, p. 120

ONGOING ASSESSMENT: Observing Students at Work

Students share seven brownies equally among four people and record their solutions, using fraction notation.

- **Do students make equal shares?**

- **Do students maintain the whole?** Do they incorrectly throw away some of the pieces?

- **Can students show and explain their solution clearly?** How do they show their solution?

- **Can students write fraction notation that represents their solution?**

As students work on this problem, ask them these questions:

- Are all your portions equal? Does it matter which portion you take?

- Have you used up all seven brownies? How do you know that all these pieces add up to seven brownies?

DIFFERENTIATION: Supporting the Range of Learners

Intervention For some students who are unsure how to begin sharing seven brownies among four people, ask them to act out what is happening in this problem. They can cut up brownies or draw smaller ones to divide them among the four people. Four paper plates or sheets of paper can represent each person so that they can actually share the portions.

Intervention Some students may begin by handing out the whole brownies and then may be unsure of what to do with the leftover brownies. Remind them of the problems with one brownie from the first sessions and how they solved those problems.

DISCUSSION

② Are These Shares Equal?

20 MIN PAIRS

Math Focus Points for Discussion

◆ Identifying equivalent fractional parts

Have three pairs briefly describe how they solved the problem. If you can, choose three pairs who have divided the brownies in different ways. Illustrate the different approaches on a piece of chart paper. If students only came up with two different approaches in your class, just write those two.

For example, if a pair says, "First we cut all the brownies in half," divide your seven rectangles in half. Continue illustrating the pair's method until you have shown the solution. Then ask the students how they can be sure that each person received the same amount. After the class agrees that the solution is fair, ask how the pair wrote the amount each person receives.

Follow the same procedure with the two other pairs. Students are likely to offer the following solutions:

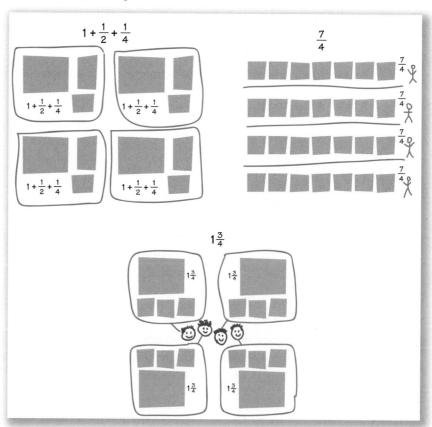

After all three pairs have shared, have everyone look at the three solutions. Write the three different answers in a row.

[Becky and Gil] figured out that each person would get $1 + \frac{1}{2} + \frac{1}{4}$, [Kenji and Arthur] figured out that each person would get $\frac{7}{4}$, and [Pilar and Kim] figured out that each person would get $1\frac{3}{4}$. Are all of these correct? Are all four people getting equal shares in each of these solutions? Does each solution mean the same thing, even though each is written differently?

Allow students to work with their partners to decide what each notation means and whether they represent the same amount of brownie. Then ask students to offer explanations. They can illustrate what they are saying by using the diagrams you drew.

Students might say:

[Comparing $\frac{7}{4}$ and $1\frac{3}{4}$] "If you put four of the fourths together from the seven fourths way, that makes one whole, and there are three fourths left, so it's the same as one and three fourths."

[Comparing $\frac{7}{4}$ and $1 + \frac{1}{2} + \frac{1}{4}$] "Four of the fourths makes one whole, and a half is equal to two fourths, and you add one more fourth, which equals three fourths."

So seven fourths equals one and three fourths. These are equivalent fractions. Let's add this to our list of Fraction Facts.

If one of these solutions is not represented in your class, and you have time, you can pose it yourself:

Here is another solution I've seen students use. Does this work? How would you write fractions to show this one?

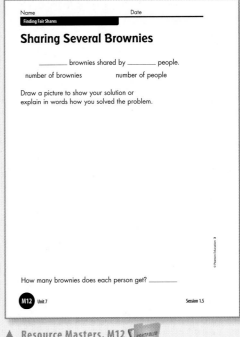

▲ **Resource Masters, M12** PORTFOLIO

ACTIVITY

20 MIN | INDIVIDUALS

3 Sharing Several Brownies

For the remainder of the session, students solve problems about sharing several brownies that are written on the board (or the chart). They record their work for each problem on Sharing Several Brownies (M12).

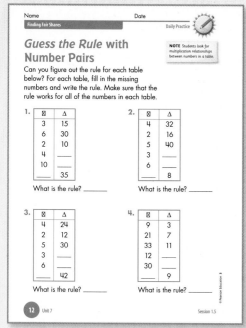

Name _____ Date _____
Finding Fair Shares   Daily Practice

Guess the Rule with Number Pairs

Can you figure out the rule for each table below? For each table, fill in the missing numbers and write the rule. Make sure that the rule works for all of the numbers in each table.

NOTE Students look for multiplication relationships between numbers in a table.

1.

⊠	Δ
3	15
6	30
2	10
4	___
10	___
___	35

What is the rule? _____

2.

⊠	Δ
4	32
2	16
5	40
3	___
6	___
___	8

What is the rule? _____

3.

⊠	Δ
4	24
2	12
5	30
3	___
6	___
___	42

What is the rule? _____

4.

⊠	Δ
9	3
21	7
33	11
12	___
30	___
___	9

What is the rule? _____

12 Unit 7   Session 1.5

▲ **Student Activity Book, p. 12**

Name _____ Date _____
Finding Fair Shares   Homework

Are These Equal?

Answer these questions. Show your work.

NOTE Students use drawings or stories to show whether these fractions are equivalent.
SMH 63, 64

1. Does $\frac{1}{2} = \frac{2}{4}$? _____
   Show how you know:

2. Does $\frac{1}{2} + \frac{1}{2} = \frac{2}{4} + \frac{2}{4}$? _____
   Show how you know:

3. Does $\frac{1}{8} + \frac{1}{8} = \frac{1}{4}$? _____
   Show how you know:

Session 1.5   Unit 7 13

▲ **Student Activity Book, p. 13**

ONGOING ASSESSMENT: Observing Students at Work

Students solve problems about sharing brownies in which each share is between one and two brownies.

- **Do students make equal shares?**

- **Can students show and explain their solution clearly?** How do they show their solution?

- **Can students write fraction notation that represents their solution?**

DIFFERENTIATION: Supporting the Range of Learners

Extension For students who need more of a challenge, you may assign a problem in which each person receives less than one brownie (e.g., share three brownies equally among four people). You may also have these students come up with more than one way to solve the problem and/or more than one way to record a solution.

Extension The following problem may challenge some students who finish quickly: Share four brownies among five people. This problem requires students to use some very small pieces and to name them with reference to the whole. Encourage students to find their own ways to solve it. Some third graders invent the following strategy: Give each person a half and then a quarter. Divide the remaining quarter into $\frac{5}{20}$. Give each person $\frac{1}{20}$.

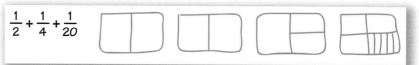

$$\frac{1}{2} + \frac{1}{4} + \frac{1}{20}$$

SESSION FOLLOW-UP
4 Daily Practice and Homework

 Daily Practice: For ongoing review, have students complete *Student Activity Book* page 12.

 Homework: On *Student Activity Book* page 13, students solve three problems about proving the equivalence of fractions and fraction expressions.

 Student Math Handbook: Students and families may use *Student Math Handbook* pages 57, 61–62, 63 for reference and review. See pages 124–127 in the back of this unit.

Assessment: Sharing Four Brownies

Math Focus Points

◆ Dividing a group into equal parts and naming the parts with fractions

◆ Dividing an area into equal parts

◆ Naming fractional parts with fractions that have numerators greater than 1 ($\frac{3}{4}$, $\frac{2}{3}$, $\frac{3}{6}$, etc.)

Today's Plan		Materials
ACTIVITY **① Sharing Many Things**	25 MIN PAIRS	• *Student Activity Book,* pp. 15–16 • Connecting cubes (as needed)
DISCUSSION **② Two Thirds of 9**	15 MIN CLASS	• M11 (from Session 1.5; as needed) • Connecting cubes (as needed)
ASSESSMENT ACTIVITY **③ Sharing Four Brownies**	✔ 20 MIN INDIVIDUALS	• M11 (from Session 1.5; as needed); M13* • Connecting cubes (as needed)
SESSION FOLLOW-UP **④ Daily Practice**		• *Student Activity Book,* p. 17 • *Student Math Handbook,* pp. 56, 57, 60, 61–62

*See *Materials to Prepare,* p. 23.

Ten-Minute Math

What Time Is It? Tell students the following story:

- I walked to school today. I left my house at 7:45 and arrived at school at 8:24. How long did it take me to walk to school?

In pairs, students share ideas about what they think. As a class, make sure that students can visualize this situation in which they are determining an interval, not an ending time. Collect ideas and focus on strategies in which students count the interval by 5s, or other chunks (such as 15 minutes from 7:45–8:00 plus 24 minutes more to 8:24, makes 39 minutes total). Ask similar questions using 6:58 as the starting time and 7:21 as the ending time.

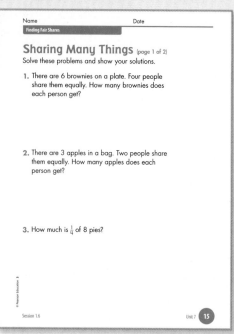

Name _____ Date _____

Finding Fair Shares

Sharing Many Things (page 1 of 2)

Solve these problems and show your solutions.

1. There are 6 brownies on a plate. Four people share them equally. How many brownies does each person get?

2. There are 3 apples in a bag. Two people share them equally. How many apples does each person get?

3. How much is $\frac{1}{4}$ of 8 pies?

Session 1.6   Unit 7   **15**

▲ **Student Activity Book, p. 15** PORTFOLIO

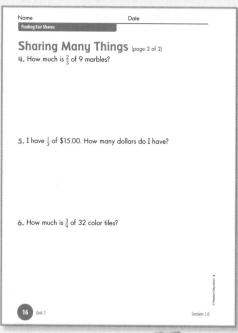

Name _____ Date _____

Finding Fair Shares

Sharing Many Things (page 2 of 2)

4. How much is $\frac{2}{3}$ of 9 marbles?

5. I have $\frac{1}{3}$ of $15.00. How many dollars do I have?

6. How much is $\frac{3}{4}$ of 32 color tiles?

16 Unit 7   Session 1.6

▲ **Student Activity Book, p. 16** PORTFOLIO

ACTIVITY

1 Sharing Many Things

25 MIN   PAIRS

Students solve problems about sharing a group of things on *Student Activity Book* pages 15–16. Although students work in pairs, each student should record their own solutions.

Students should have connecting cubes available as they work.

Students work in pairs to solve problems about sharing groups of things.

ONGOING ASSESSMENT: Observing Students at Work

Students solve two kinds of problems: equally sharing a group of objects in which each share involves a fractional part, and finding a fractional part of a group.

- **Can students create equal shares?**

- **Do students use fraction notation correctly to represent the equal shares?**

- **Can students find fractional parts of a group represented by fractions with numerators greater than one?**

15 MIN   CLASS

DISCUSSION
2 Two Thirds of 9

Math Focus Points for Discussion

◆ Dividing a group into equal parts and naming the parts with fractions

◆ Naming fractional parts with fractions that have numerators greater than 1 ($\frac{3}{4}$, $\frac{2}{3}$, $\frac{3}{6}$, etc.)

Finding $\frac{2}{3}$ of nine includes two ideas about fractions: 1) finding a fraction of a set of objects and 2) interpreting a fraction with a numerator greater than one.

Let's think about the problem: $\frac{2}{3}$ of nine. Can you tell me a story about $\frac{2}{3}$ of nine?

Collect a few examples from students. If no one provides an example, suggest a familiar context, or share an example yourself (e.g., "My soccer team has nine players on it but only $\frac{2}{3}$ showed up for practice," or "I bought nine new stickers and $\frac{2}{3}$ of them were blue").

How did you figure out what $\frac{2}{3}$ of 9 is?

Collect a few examples from students. As they share, ask them to show their solutions with cubes, brownies, or pictures. Highlight the meaning of the numerator and the denominator in this problem; that is, $\frac{2}{3}$ can represent two items out of every three.

Students might say:

"I drew 9 squares, and then I drew a circle around 3 squares, then 3 squares, and then 3 squares, so that's 3 equal groups of 3. If you take two of the groups, that's 3 plus 3, so it's 6."

"I knew that 3 times 3 is 9, so each group is 3, and 2 groups is 6."

Professional Development

① Teacher Note: Assessment: Sharing Four Brownies, p. 111

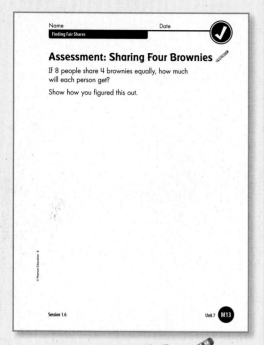

▲ **Resource Masters, M13**

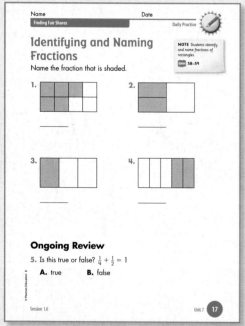

▲ **Student Activity Book, p. 17**

ASSESSMENT ACTIVITY

③ Sharing Four Brownies

20 MIN INDIVIDUALS

Students solve one assessment problem on Assessment: Sharing Four Brownies (M13). They may use drawings or cut up brownies to show their solutions.① Although this problem is not as challenging as some of the other brownie problems in Investigation 1, it shows whether students know that fractions are equal pieces and whether they can name a fractional part and write the correct fractions; in this case, $\frac{1}{2}$.

ONGOING ASSESSMENT: Observing Students at Work

Students determine fair shares when eight people share four brownies equally.

- **Can students divide a group of things into equal shares?**

- **Can students identify the fraction for each share?**

SESSION FOLLOW-UP

④ Daily Practice

Daily Practice: For reinforcement of this unit's content, have students complete *Student Activity Book* page 17.

Student Math Handbook: Students and families may use Student Math Handbook pages 56, 57, 60, 61–62 for reference and review. See pages 124–127 in the back of this unit.

Mathematical Emphases

Rational Numbers Understanding the meaning of fractions (halves, fourths, eighths, thirds, sixths) and decimal fractions (0.50, 0.25) as equal parts of a whole (an object, an area, a set of objects)

Math Focus Points

◆ Using fraction notation to record equivalencies (e.g., $\frac{3}{6} = \frac{1}{2}, \frac{1}{2} = \frac{2}{4}$)

◆ Identifying equivalent fractional parts

Rational Numbers Using representations to combine fractions (halves, fourths, eighths, thirds, and sixths)

Math Focus Points

◆ Using representations to combine fractions that sum to 1 (e.g., $\frac{1}{4} + \frac{3}{4} = 1, \frac{1}{3} + \frac{1}{3} + \frac{1}{3} = 1, \frac{1}{2} + \frac{1}{4} + \frac{1}{4} = 1$)

◆ Using representations to combine fractions to equal other fractions ($\frac{1}{2} = \frac{1}{3} + \frac{1}{6}$)

Many Ways to Make a Share

	Student Activity Book	Student Math Handbook	Professional Development: Read Ahead of Time	
SESSION 2.1 p. 60				
Making Cookie Shares Students find ways to make one whole with combinations of halves, thirds, and sixths by using pattern blocks. They also find combinations of fractions that equal $\frac{1}{2}$, $\frac{1}{3}$, and $\frac{2}{3}$. They write equations for these combinations.	18–19	63, 64	• **Teacher Note:** Visualizing Fraction Equivalencies, p. 113	
SESSION 2.2 p. 69				
The Fraction Cookie Game Students play a game in which they combine fractional parts to create wholes and find fraction equivalencies.	20–21	63, 64; G11–G12	• **Dialogue Box:** Playing the *Fraction Cookie Game*, p. 122	
SESSION 2.3 p. 74				
Assessment: Many Ways to Make a Share Students discuss whether a combination of two fractions equals a half and find equivalencies for a variety of fractions ($\frac{1}{2}$, $\frac{1}{3}$, $\frac{2}{3}$, $\frac{1}{4}$, $\frac{3}{4}$). They are assessed on their knowledge of common equivalent fractions (such as $\frac{3}{6} = \frac{1}{2}$ and $\frac{1}{3} = \frac{2}{6}$) and on combining fractions to equal 1 and other fractions.	23–24	58–59, 63, 64; G11–G12		
SESSION 2.4 p. 80				
Making Half-Yellow Designs Students find half of different pattern block designs and continue to work on finding equivalencies.	23, 25–27	63, 64; G11–G12		

Ten-Minute Math See page 16 for an overview.

Today's Number
- No materials needed

What Time Is It?
- Demonstration clock
- Student clocks

Materials to Gather	Materials to Prepare
• **T92, Hexagon Cookies** 🖥 ✓ • **Overhead Pattern Blocks** (1 set) • **Colored pencils, markers, or crayons** (red, blue, green, yellow) • **Transparency markers in red, blue, green, and yellow** • **Chart: "Fraction Facts"** (from Session 1.3)	• **M16, Hexagon Cookies** Make several copies for activity extension and for use in the rest of the investigation. (at least 3 per student) ✓ • **Pattern Blocks** Prepare sets of pattern blocks by removing the orange squares and the white rhombuses from each set. (1 bucket per 4–6 students)
• **T92, Hexagon Cookies** 🖥 • **M16, Hexagon Cookies** (from Session 2.1; as needed) • **M14–M15, *Fraction Cookie*** (optional) • **Overhead Pattern Blocks** • **Fraction number cubes in two colors** (1 per pair) • **Pattern Blocks** (1 bucket per 5–6 students) • **Colored pencils, markers, or crayons** (red, blue, green, yellow) • **Chart: "Fraction Facts"** (from Session 1.3)	• **Fraction Number Cubes** If you are not using manufactured fraction number cubes, small blank cubes such as inch cubes can be substituted. You will need two colors of cubes—2 in one color and 1 in another color for each set of 3. Label the faces of these cubes with the following fractions: $$\frac{1}{2} \quad \frac{1}{2} \quad \frac{1}{3} \quad \frac{1}{6} \quad \frac{2}{3} \quad \frac{5}{6}$$ One way to do this is to write the fractions on dot stickers and affix them to the cube faces.
• **M16, Hexagon Cookies** (from Session 2.1; as needed) • **Chart: "Fraction Facts"** (from Session 1.3) • **Pattern Blocks** (1 bucket per 5–6 students) • **Students' Fraction Sets** (optional) • **Fraction number cubes in two colors** (1 per pair) • **Colored pencils, markers, or crayons** (red, blue, green, yellow)	• **M11, Small Brownies** Make copies. (as needed) • **M17, Assessment Checklist: Many Ways to Make a Share** ✓ Make copies. (as needed)
• **M16, Hexagon Cookies** (from Session 2.1) • **M17, Assessment Checklist: Many Ways to Make a Share** ✓ (from Session 2.3) • **T93, Triangle Paper** 🖥 • **Overhead Pattern Blocks** • **Pattern Blocks** (1 bucket per 5–6 students) • **Fraction number cubes in two colors** (1 per pair) • **Colored pencils, markers, or crayons** (red, blue, green, yellow)	• **M18, Triangle Paper** Make copies. (1 per student plus extras) • **Half-Yellow Designs** Make two half-yellow designs on the transparency of Triangle Paper (T93). See examples in Session 2.4.

🖥 Overhead Transparency　　　✓ Checklist Available

Making Cookie Shares

Math Focus Points

◆ Using representations to combine fractions that sum to 1 (e.g., $\frac{1}{4} + \frac{3}{4} = 1, \frac{1}{3} + \frac{1}{3} + \frac{1}{3} = 1, \frac{1}{2} + \frac{1}{4} + \frac{1}{4} = 1$)

◆ Using fraction notation to record equivalencies (e.g., $\frac{3}{6} = \frac{1}{2}, \frac{1}{2} = \frac{2}{4}$)

◆ Using representations to combine fractions to equal other fractions ($\frac{1}{2} = \frac{1}{3} + \frac{1}{6}$)

Today's Plan		Materials
ACTIVITY **① Cutting Up Cookies**	25 MIN CLASS INDIVIDUALS	• *Student Activity Book*, p. 18 • M16*; T92 • Pattern blocks*; overhead pattern blocks; colored pencils, markers, or crayons (red, blue, green, yellow); transparency markers in red, blue, green and yellow
ACTIVITY **② Writing Equations**	15 MIN CLASS	• *Student Activity Book*, p. 18 • T92 (with students' solutions)
DISCUSSION **③ How Many Ways Can You Make a Half?**	20 MIN CLASS PAIRS	• *Student Activity Book*, p. 18 • Chart: "Fraction Facts" (from Session 1.3); pattern blocks
SESSION FOLLOW-UP **④ Daily Practice**		• *Student Activity Book*, p. 19 • *Student Math Handbook*, pp. 63, 64

*See *Materials to Prepare*, p. 59.

Ten-Minute Math

Today's Number Students create expressions that equal 605 using addition and subtraction. Collect expressions that include a variety of different-sized numbers, different lengths, and ones that include only addition, only subtraction and a combination of both. Ask students:

• How can you be sure this expression equals 605? Explain your strategy so the rest of us can understand it.

ACTIVITY

1 Cutting Up Cookies

25 MIN   CLASS   INDIVIDUALS

Explain to students that they will now be using pattern blocks, which they can think of as cookies, to identify and combine fractions.

Show students the yellow hexagon overhead pattern block on the overhead projector.

Let's say that this yellow pattern block is a cookie. How could we make a cookie that's the same size and shape as this with other pattern blocks? Here are the pattern blocks we have to work with.

Show students the red trapezoid, blue rhombus, and green triangle overhead pattern blocks.

How many blue pattern blocks do we need to cover a yellow hexagon cookie completely? How many red pattern blocks? Green pattern blocks? Try each of these with your own pattern blocks.

Give students a few minutes to make each of these combinations with pattern blocks and to compare what they found with their neighbors. Then collect students' solutions. From their experience with pattern blocks in younger grades, it is likely that students will quickly determine that two red trapezoids, three blue rhombuses, or six green triangles each make a yellow hexagon.

You've discovered that two red trapezoids make a yellow hexagon cookie. What fraction of a yellow pattern block cookie is each of these red pattern blocks? What fraction is the blue pattern block? The green pattern block?

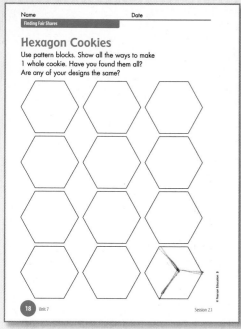

▲ **Student Activity Book, p. 18;
Resource Masters, M16; T92**

As students name these, write them on the board with fraction notation.

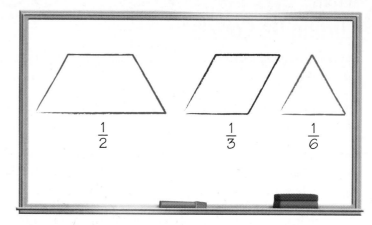

If we think of these as parts of cookies, we can say that the red piece represents one out of two equal pieces of a hexagon cookie, so it's one half. A blue piece is one out of three equal pieces of a hexagon cookie, and a green is one out of six equal pieces.

Show students the transparency of Hexagon Cookies (T92).

You're going to have a sheet filled with pictures of pattern block hexagons. Your task is to find many different combinations of red, blue, and green pattern blocks that will cover a yellow hexagon cookie exactly.

Students use pattern blocks to find as many different ways as they can to cover the yellow hexagon cookie. Make sure that students understand that they can now combine different shapes. Have them record their solutions on *Student Activity Book* page 18 by drawing the smaller pattern block pieces onto the hexagons. As students draw all the ways to divide the hexagons that they find, they should also write the corresponding fractions in each of the pieces.

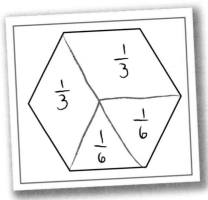

Sample Student Work

Students should check their work to make sure that none of their solutions are the same. Some students may decide that two solutions are not the same if they have the same pieces but are arranged differently. If so, ask questions to help them think about whether these are really different *combinations* of fractions.

I see that you have two cookies that both have two blues and two greens. What's different about each of these? What's the same? What fractions are you combining in each of these solutions?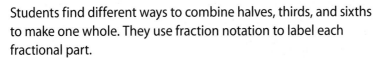

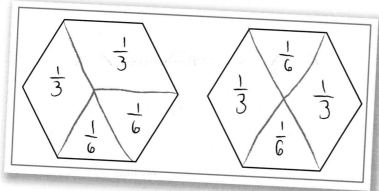

Sample Student Work

Collect students' solutions on the transparency of Hexagon Cookies (T92) while they are working, either by inviting students to come up and draw one of their solutions or by passing the transparency around. If you have red, blue, and green transparency pens, students may use these to indicate the corresponding pattern blocks.

ONGOING ASSESSMENT: Observing Students at Work

Students find different ways to combine halves, thirds, and sixths to make one whole. They use fraction notation to label each fractional part.

- **Do students understand that if two red trapezoids combine to make a whole, each piece is $\frac{1}{2}$?** Similarly, do they understand that each blue rhombus is a third because three of them make a whole, and each green triangle is a sixth because six of them make a whole?

- **Can students use a combination of different-sized fractions to make a whole?**

Teaching Note

① **Same or Different?** Students will encounter mathematical activities in which different arrangements of the same mathematical objects—shapes or numbers, for example—are considered the same or different, depending on the mathematical purpose. For example, 6×3 is the same as 3×6 in that both have the same product. However, these expressions may represent different situations: 6 bags with 3 marbles in each bag is different from 3 bags with 6 marbles in each bag. Shape arrangements using the same set of shapes may also be considered the same or different, depending on what is needed in a mathematical situation. In this activity, students are looking for different *combinations* of fractional parts that make a whole, without regard for their order or arrangement. Let students know that for this activity, you want them to consider two combinations made with the same pieces to be the same solution, even though in some other context, it could be important to find all the different arrangements.

As you observe students working on this task, ask questions such as the following to help students connect the pattern block pieces to fraction notation:

- Which pattern block is a half of a hexagon cookie?

- What fraction of the hexagon is the blue pattern block?

- How many green triangles did you use to make the whole? What fraction is the green piece then?

DIFFERENTIATION: Supporting the Range of Learners

Extension Students who finish quickly may investigate all the different ways to cover two hexagon cookies, or two wholes, with combinations of halves, thirds, and sixths. They may record these on another copy of Hexagon Cookies (M16) and write addition equations for these combinations.

ACTIVITY

② Writing Equations

15 MIN   CLASS

Bring the class back together to look at the transparency completed with their solutions. Students may copy any solutions that they do not have on their own sheets and also may check for missing solutions on the transparency. There are seven different ways to cover the yellow hexagon cookie with two or more pattern block pieces, if different arrangements of the same pieces are counted as the same. (See one student's sample solutions on the next page.)

Direct students' attention to one of the solutions on the transparency, preferably one that shows a combination of each of the three pattern blocks. Ask students how they would represent this with fraction notation.

How can we write an addition equation that describes combining this half, this third, and this sixth to make one whole?

As one or more students respond, write the addition equation under the corresponding hexagon on the transparency (i.e., $\frac{1}{2} + \frac{1}{3} + \frac{1}{6} = 1$).

If needed, write an equation for one more hexagon as a class. Then, students write addition equations that describe each of their hexagons on *Student Activity Book* page 18, as in the illustration of one student's work below.

Sample Student Work

![check mark icon] **ONGOING ASSESSMENT: Observing Students at Work**

Students write equations that represent how combinations of fractions make one whole.

- **Can students write addition equations to describe their wholes?**

- **Are students using fraction notation correctly?**

③ DISCUSSION

How Many Ways Can You Make a Half?

20 MIN CLASS PAIRS

Math Focus Points for Discussion

◆ Using representations to combine fractions to equal other fractions ($\frac{1}{2} = \frac{1}{3} + \frac{1}{6}$)

When there are about 20 minutes left in the session, ask students to share some of the fraction equations they wrote to describe their hexagons.

We found many ways of making a whole yellow hexagon cookie. What are some of the equations that you wrote next to your hexagons? Let's add these to our list of Fraction Facts.

Collect and record a number of equations in the section of the chart titled "Halves, Thirds, and Sixths." Then ask students to consider how they might make fractions of pattern block cookies that are less than one whole.

You made a whole cookie with fractional parts in several ways. Which pattern block is half a cookie? What are ways you can make one half of a cookie with other fractional pieces? How would you write these ways as equations?

Give students a few minutes to find examples with pattern blocks, before you ask for ideas to record.

Collect students' suggestions, and add them to the "Fraction Facts" list ($\frac{1}{3} + \frac{1}{6} = \frac{1}{2}$ and $\frac{1}{6} + \frac{1}{6} + \frac{1}{6} = \frac{1}{2}$).

Which pattern block is one third of a cookie? Can you make one third of a yellow cookie by using other combination of pieces? (two green triangles)

Can you show one fourth of a yellow cookie with the pattern blocks?

Give students a few minutes to try to make one fourth of a yellow cookie with the pattern blocks, and then ask for their ideas. Some students may suggest using some combination of four blocks (e.g., two green blocks and two blue blocks) and calling one of the pieces "one fourth." If students do not bring up this reasoning, you may want to bring it up yourself and ask students what they think about it.

Someone once said to me that they could show fourths with pattern blocks like this [cover a yellow hexagon with two green triangles and two blue rhombuses]. Do these pieces show fourths? Why or why not?

Not equal pieces

Students might say:

 "They can't be fourths because the blue pieces are much bigger than the green pieces, and fourths have to be the same size."

Other students may say that they can show one fourth of a hexagon but not with the pattern block pieces. For example, a student might draw fourths on a hexagon shape as follows:

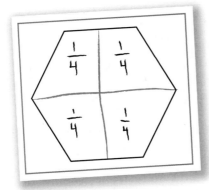

Sample Student Work

 "I didn't use pattern blocks. I drew the yellow hexagon cookie and divided it in half from corner to corner. That made two trapezoids. Then I drew a line down the middle of each."

 "A fourth would be a triangle and a half. A half of a cookie is three triangles, and half of that would be one whole triangle and then half of another triangle. It's like when we shared the brownies."

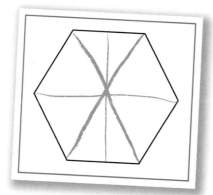

Sample Student Work

Professional Development

2 Teacher Note: Visualizing Fraction Equivalencies, p. 113

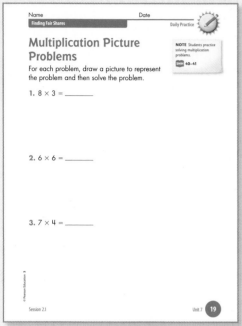

▲ Student Activity Book, p. 19

What about two thirds? What does "two thirds" of a cookie mean? How can you make that with pattern block pieces?

For the rest of the session, students work with partners to find ways to make $\frac{2}{3}$ with pattern blocks and write equations that match their work. If there is time, suggest that they also try $\frac{5}{6}$. Students may add some of their equations to the "Fraction Facts" list as they find them.

Students will work more with these equivalencies in the next session.**2**

SESSION FOLLOW-UP

4 Daily Practice

Daily Practice: For ongoing review, have students complete *Student Activity Book* page 19.

Student Math Handbook: Students and families may use *Student Math Handbook* pages 63, 64 for reference and review. See pages 124–127 in the back of this unit.

The Fraction Cookie Game

Math Focus Points

◆ Using representations to combine fractions that sum to 1
(e.g., $\frac{1}{4} + \frac{3}{4} = 1, \frac{1}{3} + \frac{1}{3} + \frac{1}{3} = 1, \frac{1}{2} + \frac{1}{4} + \frac{1}{4} = 1$)

◆ Identifying equivalent fractional parts

◆ Using representations to combine fractions to equal other fractions
($\frac{1}{2} = \frac{1}{3} + \frac{1}{6}$)

Vocabulary

equivalent fractions

Today's Plan		Materials
ACTIVITY **①** Introducing the *Fraction Cookie* Game	15 MIN CLASS	• T92 ; M14–M15 (optional) • Overhead pattern blocks; fraction number cubes*
ACTIVITY **②** The *Fraction Cookie* Game	35 MIN PAIRS	• M16 (from Session 2.1) • Fraction number cubes in 2 colors; pattern blocks; colored pencils, markers, or crayons (red, blue, green, yellow)
DISCUSSION **③** Finding Fraction Equivalencies	10 MIN CLASS	• T92 • Overhead pattern blocks; Chart: "Fraction Facts" (from Session 1.3)
SESSION FOLLOW-UP **④** Daily Practice and Homework		• *Student Activity Book,* pp. 20–21 • *Student Math Handbook,* pp. 63, 64; G11–G12

*See *Materials to Prepare,* p. 59.

Ten-Minute Math

Today's Number Students use at least three numbers to create expressions that equal 700. They must use both addition and subtraction in each expression; for example, $525 + 75 + 300 - 200 = 700$. Collect a few expressions to write on the board and ask students to explain how they know they equal 700.

Differentiation

Differentiation

1 English Language Learners Check in with English Language Learners after this whole-class demonstration to make sure they understand what was demonstrated and how to play the game. Make sure students understand how to identify the fewest pieces. Show two groups of pieces and point to the group that has the fewest pieces. Then ask students to do the same. Review the names of shapes if necessary. You may want to play one short round of the game with English Language Learners, using descriptive sentences and having students repeat the sentences to describe the moves.

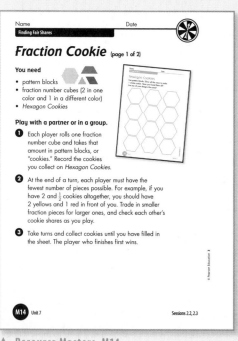

▲ Resource Masters, M14

ACTIVITY

1 Introducing the *Fraction Cookie* Game

15 MIN   CLASS

Introduce the *Fraction Cookie* game to the whole class. Explain that in this game, students collect pieces of pattern block cookies. The basic game is played with one fraction number cube. On each turn, players roll a number cube and add the exact amount of their roll to their cookies. They use a copy of Hexagon Cookies (M16) to keep track of their cookies as they collect them. Have available copies of *Fraction Cookie* (M14–M15) as needed.

Demonstrate with the transparency of Hexagon Cookies (T92). Roll one fraction number cube and put the overhead pattern block representing that fraction on the overhead. Roll again, and add the new block or blocks to your display. Then introduce students to the idea of "trading."

An important rule of the *Fraction Cookie* game is that you must always have as few pieces as possible when you've finished collecting cookie pieces on your turn. Let's look at my cookies so far.

The following is an example; use whatever fractions you rolled in your demonstration to make this same point.

I rolled $\frac{1}{3}$ on my first turn, so I took a blue rhombus. Then I rolled $\frac{2}{6}$ on my second turn, so I took two green triangles. Do I have the fewest pieces possible in my cookie? How could I trade so that I have fewer?

This aspect of the game gives students an opportunity to recognize and make use of equivalent fractions and equivalent combinations of fractions. You may roll a few more rounds on your own cookie display to make sure that students understand the rule about trading before they play in pairs.

Demonstrate an example in which students must break a fraction apart to complete one hexagon and part of another. For example, if $\frac{1}{2}$ of a hexagon is covered and a player rolls $\frac{5}{6}$, fill the remaining $\frac{1}{2}$ and then $\frac{2}{6}$ of another hexagon.**1**

ACTIVITY

The *Fraction Cookie* Game

35 MIN   PAIRS

Students play the *Fraction Cookie* game in pairs. Each student uses Hexagon Cookies (M16) to place their "cookie pieces" as they collect them. If yellow hexagons are in short supply, students may use the sheet for recording their completed cookies. Each time a cookie is complete, the player removes the blocks from the sheet and colors in or puts an **X** on the cookie. Decide as a class when a game is complete, perhaps when a sheet of hexagon cookies has been filled up.

Remind students that players must trade equivalent fractions so that they always have the fewest pieces possible.❷

Professional Development

❷ **Dialogue Box:** Playing the *Fraction Cookie* Game, p. 122

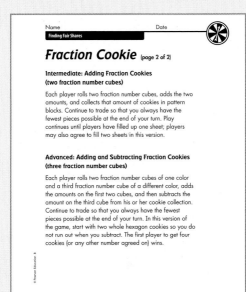

▲ Resource Masters, M15

Students play the Fraction Cookie *game to investigate equivalent fractions.*

ONGOING ASSESSMENT: Observing Students at Work

Students construct wholes with combinations of halves, thirds, and sixths and practice recognizing equivalent fractional parts.

- **Do students recognize how much of a hexagon pattern block is designated by the fractions on the fraction number cube** $(\frac{1}{2}, \frac{1}{3}, \frac{1}{6}, \frac{2}{3}, \frac{5}{6})$**?**

- **Do students recognize equivalent fractional amounts?** For example, when they roll $\frac{1}{2}$, do they know that they can take one red block $(\frac{1}{2})$ or three green blocks $(\frac{3}{6})$?

• **Can students break some fractions apart, adding one part to complete a whole and using the other part to begin the next whole?** (For example, a student already has $\frac{5}{6}$ of a cookie and rolls $\frac{1}{3}$. Can she take that $\frac{1}{3}$ as two green blocks so that she uses $\frac{1}{6}$ of a cookie to complete the whole and the other $\frac{1}{6}$ to start a new cookie?)

DISCUSSION

③ Finding Fraction Equivalencies

10 MIN   CLASS

Math Focus Points for Discussion

◆ Identifying equivalent fractional parts

◆ Using representations to combine fractions to equal other fractions
$(\frac{1}{2} = \frac{1}{3} + \frac{1}{6})$

Bring the class together and ask students to talk about some of the "trades" they made as they were playing the game.

Who can give us an example of when you had to make a trade so that you would end up with as few pattern block pieces as possible? How much of a hexagon did you start with? What did you roll? How did you make the trade?

Students might say:

"I started with a red and a green. I rolled five sixths, so I took five greens. Two greens filled up my cookie, but then I had three greens left over and that was too many pieces. So I traded them for a red."

Help students make the connection between the pattern block pieces and the fractions they represent by asking questions or restating students' explanations. You may also find it helpful to use the overhead pattern blocks to act out students' moves as they describe them.

[Oscar] started with a red block and a green block. How could we name those pieces as fractions? (a half and a sixth) How much of the hexagon did he have already? (two thirds) What pieces did he need to make a whole cookie? (either one blue or two greens) What fraction did he need to finish his cookie then? ($\frac{1}{3}$ or $\frac{2}{6}$)

Ask students to identify the fraction equivalencies that are represented by the trades they made. For example:

Why was [Jung] able to trade three green blocks for a red block? Can anyone explain it, using the fraction names for each of these pattern block pieces?

Some students may say that they can make the trade because the pieces match; that is, using the above example, they can lay three green blocks perfectly on top of a red block. Encourage students to also think about the relationship between the fractions that the blocks represent.

If we are calling this red trapezoid a half because it's half of a hexagon, and this green triangle a sixth because six of them make up a whole hexagon, what does this trade tell us about halves and sixths? How many sixths are equal to one half?

As students agree that, for example, three sixths are equal to one half, check to see whether this equation (e.g., $\frac{3}{6} = \frac{1}{2}$) is already on the Fraction Facts Chart; if not, write it there. Then ask students to contribute other equations that represent trades they made in the game, such as $\frac{1}{3} = \frac{2}{6}$ or $\frac{1}{2} = \frac{1}{3} + \frac{1}{6}$.

We call fractions that are equal to one another, such as one third and two sixths, **equivalent fractions**. *Are there other equivalent fractions you can think of, maybe from your brownies or Fraction Sets?*

Spend the last few minutes recording any equivalent fractions that students may remember from previous work, such as $\frac{1}{2} = \frac{2}{4}$ from their work with Fraction Sets, on the appropriate Fraction Facts Chart.

SESSION FOLLOW-UP

Daily Practice and Homework

 Daily Practice: For ongoing review, have students complete *Student Activity Book* page 20.

 Homework: On *Student Activity Book* page 21, students identify and order two sets of unit fractions.

 Student Math Handbook: Students and families may use *Student Math Handbook* pages 63, 64 and G11–G12 for reference and review. See pages 124–127 in the back of this unit.

▲ **Student Activity Book, p. 20**

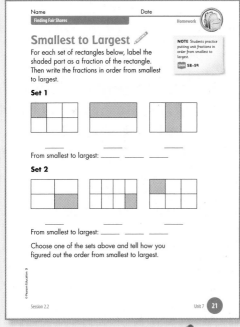

▲ **Student Activity Book, p. 21**

Assessment: Many Ways to Make a Share

Math Focus Points

◆ Using representations to combine fractions that sum to 1 (e.g., $\frac{1}{4} + \frac{3}{4} = 1, \frac{1}{3} + \frac{1}{3} + \frac{1}{3} = 1, \frac{1}{2} + \frac{1}{4} + \frac{1}{4} = 1$)

◆ Using representations to combine fractions to equal other fractions ($\frac{1}{2} = \frac{1}{3} + \frac{1}{6}$)

◆ Identifying equivalent fractional parts

Today's Plan		Materials
DISCUSSION **① Is It a Half?** 15 MIN CLASS PAIRS		• M11 (as needed)*; M16 (from Session 2.1; as needed) • Chart: "Fraction Facts" (from Session 1.3); pattern blocks: Students' Fraction Sets (as needed)

MATH WORKSHOP
② Equivalent Fractions
②Ⓐ Assessment: Many Ways to Make a Share
②Ⓑ The *Fraction Cookie* Game
45 MIN
		②Ⓐ • *Student Activity Book*, p. 23
		     • M17* ✓
		②Ⓑ • M14–M15 (from Session 2.2)
		     • Fraction number cubes in two colors (from Session 2.2); pattern blocks; colored pencils, markers, or crayons

SESSION FOLLOW-UP **③ Daily Practice**		• *Student Activity Book*, p. 24 • *Student Math Handbook*, pp. 58–59, 63, 64; G11–G12

*See *Materials to Prepare*, p. 59.

Ten-Minute Math

Today's Number Students create expressions that equal 288, using only subtraction. For example: $308 - 20 = 288$, and $388 - 50 - 50 = 288$. Write examples on the board and have students share their strategies for writing each expression.

DISCUSSION

Is It a Half?

15 MIN   CLASS   PAIRS

Math Focus Points for Discussion

◆ Using representations to combine fractions to equal other fractions
($\frac{1}{2} = \frac{1}{3} + \frac{1}{6}$)

Write the following equation on the board or overhead:

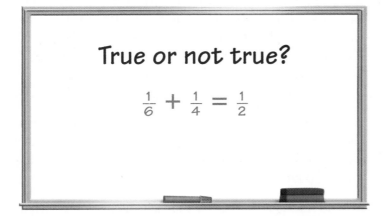

True or not true?

$$\frac{1}{6} + \frac{1}{4} = \frac{1}{2}$$

Is this a true equation? Does one sixth plus one fourth equal one half? Talk about this with your partner for a minute. Think about how you would show that it's either true or not true. Think about the hexagon cookies or brownies.

Give students a few minutes to discuss this in pairs and make any drawings or use any materials they might need. Make sure that pattern blocks, copies of Small Brownies (M11) and Hexagon Cookies (M16) are easily available. As you are listening to their discussions, notice what reasoning they are using.

Students might say:

"I made fourths on one brownie and sixths on another brownie. Then I cut them out and I put one fourth and one sixth together, and they don't cover a half. It's too small."

"I know that one fourth and one fourth is a half, so it can't be true that one sixth and one fourth are a half too—they're just different."

▲ **Student Activity Book, p. 23** PORTFOLIO

"When we used the pattern blocks, one green and one blue is the same as a half, and the green is a sixth, but the blue's not a fourth—it's a third."

Bring the class back together and ask two or three pairs of students to share their thinking, including any representations they may have used. If there is disagreement about whether the equation is true, give students the opportunity to convince each other by sharing their representations. Some students may need to act out the problem to see whether they can make a sixth and a fourth equal a half. When the class has come to agreement, wrap up the discussion by introducing students to the Math Workshop activity, Many Ways to Make a Share.

In Math Workshop today, you're going to find more combinations of fractions that equal other fractions, and you should keep thinking about how you would prove that the combinations you come up with are true. Could you show them with pattern blocks, or brownies, or drawings? How do you picture these fractions in your mind?

Remind students that they have already discussed and recorded several ways to make a whole and a half, and that they may include a few of these as well as other ways they discovered in their work since those discussions. Also let students know that they can use any of the fraction tools they have been working with (brownies, Fraction Sets, or pattern blocks) to help them find equivalencies for each fraction on *Student Activity Book* page 23.

MATH WORKSHOP

45 MIN

② Equivalent Fractions

Students work on two activities. The first, Many Ways to Make a Share, focuses on combining smaller fractions to make other fractions. The second, the *Fraction Cookie* game, focuses on combining fractions to make one whole. Students will continue working on both of these activities in the Math Workshop in the next session.

This Math Workshop includes an observed assessment of students' knowledge of the fraction equivalencies they have been using so far in this unit. See the section below for more information about conducting this assessment.

2A Assessment: Many Ways to Make a Share

INDIVIDUALS   PAIRS

Working alone or with a partner, students find fraction equivalencies on *Student Activity Book* page 23. There are six problems on this page that all students should do, and then two challenge problems that you may expect some, but not all students, to do. Encourage students either to imagine or work physically with pattern block cookies, paper brownies, or Fraction Sets to help them find more than one equivalency for each fraction, especially for fourths and eighths. Students may add to the class list of Fraction Facts as they discover more equivalencies that have not yet been mentioned.

This observed assessment addresses two of the benchmarks for this unit:

Benchmark 2: Identify equivalent fractions (e.g., $\frac{3}{6} = \frac{1}{2}$ and $\frac{1}{3} = \frac{2}{6}$).

Benchmark 3: Find combinations of fractions that are equal to one and to other fractions (e.g., $\frac{3}{6} + \frac{1}{2} = 1$; $\frac{1}{6} + \frac{1}{6} = \frac{1}{3}$; and $\frac{1}{3} + \frac{1}{6} = \frac{1}{2}$).

At this point in the unit, students should be familiar with a number of equivalent fractions without having to construct them each time. These include equivalencies for $\frac{1}{2}$ ($\frac{2}{4}$, $\frac{3}{6}$, and $\frac{4}{8}$) and $\frac{1}{3}$ ($\frac{2}{6}$), as well as fractions that are equivalent to 1 ($\frac{2}{2}$, $\frac{3}{3}$, $\frac{6}{6}$, and so on). Students should be using these in the expressions they write on *Student Activity Book* page 23. As you observe students working on this activity, record your observations on Assessment Checklist: Many Ways to Make a Share (M17). Record a few examples of equivalent fractions that each student knows. You do not need to record every combination that students use in their work; just observe whether they are able to combine fractions to equal one as well as some other fractions.

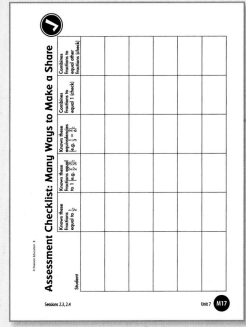

▲ **Resource Masters, M17** ☑

This observed assessment should take no more than a minute or two for each student over the two days of Math Workshop. If there is not enough time to meet with all students during Math Workshop, plan to meet with the remaining students some time outside math time or while students are working on other activities in the next investigation.

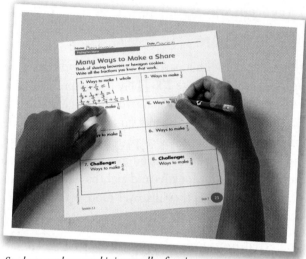

Students work on combining smaller fractions to make other fractions up to 1 whole.

ONGOING ASSESSMENT: Observing Students at Work

Students use knowledge of common equivalent fractions (e.g., $\frac{3}{6} = \frac{1}{2}$; $\frac{2}{3} = \frac{4}{6}$) and combinations of fractions that are equal to one and to other fractions (e.g., $\frac{3}{3} = 1, \frac{1}{4} + \frac{1}{4} = \frac{1}{2}, \frac{1}{3} + \frac{1}{6} = \frac{1}{2}$) to construct a whole and find a variety of ways to represent given fractions.

- **Do students recognize that a fraction in which the numerator is half of the denominator is equal to $\frac{1}{2}$ (such as $\frac{2}{4}, \frac{3}{6}, \frac{4}{8}$)?** Do they use this knowledge to write equations for $\frac{1}{2}$, one whole (such as $\frac{1}{2} + \frac{3}{6} = 1$), or any other fractions (such as $\frac{4}{8} + \frac{1}{4} = \frac{3}{4}$)?

- **Do students know other common fraction equivalencies, such as $\frac{1}{3} = \frac{2}{6}, \frac{2}{3} = \frac{4}{6}$, or $\frac{2}{8} = \frac{1}{4}$?** Do they use these in writing fraction equations?

- **Can students combine fractions to equal a whole?** To equal other fractions?

DIFFERENTIATION: Supporting the Range of Learners

Intervention If there are some students who are not yet sure about these basic equivalencies, they should continue to work with fraction tools to construct them and make a list for themselves that they can refer back to.

Extension To make some of the fractions that are larger than $\frac{1}{2}$, challenge students to combine fourths and sixths or eighths and sixths (for example, one way to make $\frac{3}{4}$ would be $\frac{3}{6} + \frac{1}{4}$).

2B The *Fraction Cookie* Game

 PAIRS

For complete details about this activity, see Session 2.2, pages 70–71. Additionally, you may want to consider the following note.

DIFFERENTIATION: Supporting the Range of Learners

Extension There are two more levels of the *Fraction Cookie* game for those students who have had experience with the basic game and are ready for more of a challenge. Watch for students who can quickly substitute equivalent fractions instead of having to reconstruct each equivalency. These students should move on to the intermediate game, *Adding Fraction Cookies.* In this variation, players roll two fraction number cubes. The sum of the amounts determines how much of a cookie to take. See the directions for this variation on the *Fraction Cookie* game (M14–M15).

SESSION FOLLOW-UP

3 Daily Practice

 Daily Practice: For reinforcement of this unit's content, have students complete *Student Activity Book* page 24.

 Student Math Handbook: Students and families may use *Student Math Handbook* pages 58–59, 63, 64 and G11–G12 for reference and review. See pages 124–127 in the back of this unit.

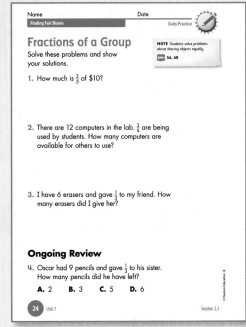

Name _____ Date _____
Finding Fair Shares   Daily Practice

Fractions of a Group
Solve these problems and show your solutions.

NOTE Students solve problems about sharing objects equally.
56, 60

1. How much is $\frac{3}{5}$ of $10?

2. There are 12 computers in the lab. $\frac{3}{4}$ are being used by students. How many computers are available for others to use?

3. I have 6 erasers and gave $\frac{1}{3}$ to my friend. How many erasers did I give her?

Ongoing Review
4. Oscar had 9 pencils and gave $\frac{1}{3}$ to his sister. How many pencils did he have left?
   A. 2   **B.** 3   **C.** 5   **D.** 6

24 Unit 7   Session 2.3

▲ **Student Activity Book, p. 24**

Making Half–Yellow Designs

Math Focus Points

◆ Using representations to combine fractions that sum to 1 (e.g., $\frac{1}{4} + \frac{3}{4} = 1$, $\frac{1}{3} + \frac{1}{3} + \frac{1}{3} = 1$, $\frac{1}{2} + \frac{1}{4} + \frac{1}{4} = 1$)

◆ Using representations to combine fractions to equal other fractions ($\frac{1}{2} = \frac{1}{3} + \frac{1}{6}$)

Today's Plan		Materials
ACTIVITY **1** **Introducing Half-Yellow Designs**	20 MIN CLASS PAIRS	• T93 • Half-Yellow Designs*
MATH WORKSHOP **2** **Equivalent Fractions** **2A** Half-Yellow Designs **2B** Assessment: Many Ways to Make a Share **2C** The *Fraction Cookie* Game	40 MIN	**2A** • *Student Activity Book,* p. 25 • M18* • Pattern blocks; colored pencils or markers (red, blue, green, and yellow) **2B** • *Student Activity Book,* p. 23 • M17 ☑ (from Session 2.3) **2C** • M16 (from Session 2.1) • Fraction number cubes in 2 colors*; pattern blocks; colored pencils, markers, or crayons (red, blue, green, yellow)
SESSION FOLLOW-UP **3** **Daily Practice and Homework**		• *Student Activity Book,* pp. 26–27 • *Student Math Handbook,* pp. 63, 64; G11–G12

*See *Materials to Prepare,* p. 59.

Ten-Minute Math

Today's Number Students use coin values (5¢, 10¢, 25¢, and 50¢) and dollars to create expressions that equal $9.50. They must include multiplication in each expression they create. Remind them to use parentheses to make clear which numbers each operation involves; for example, $(9 \times \$0.50) + (5 \times \$1.00) = \$9.50$.

ACTIVITY

Introducing Half-Yellow Designs

20 MIN CLASS PAIRS

Show the first example of a Half-Yellow Design (with one yellow block) that you made ahead of time. Without naming it, ask the class to consider how much of the whole design is yellow.

*I want to show you a design that I made with pattern blocks. I used several different colors and shapes in my design. My question for you is, how much of this design is yellow? Think of this design as a fancy cookie. If I eat the yellow part, how much of the cookie did I eat? What fraction would be the amount of the whole cookie I ate?*❶

Give students a few minutes to consider the question in pairs. They may reconstruct your design with their own pattern blocks if that will help them. In order to think about this, students need to change their thinking of the yellow hexagon as "one whole" and consider it instead as part of a larger whole.

Students might say:

"If we put the red and green pieces together, they make another whole hexagon. That's two hexagons, so one hexagon is half, and that's the yellow part."

Teaching Note

❶ **Half-Yellow Designs** Making a design that is half yellow is a more difficult task than determining half of an already-drawn shape. For example, students may think that half the *number* of blocks should be yellow. To help them think through their ideas, ask them to think about their whole design as one cookie: "If one person takes the yellow blocks in the design and one person takes the other blocks, do they have the same amount of cookie?"

Differentiation

② English Language Learners If English Language Learners are unable to put their explanation into words, assist by asking several yes/no questions or questions that require a one or two-word answer: How many blocks do you have? How many yellow blocks do you have? Can these two reds cover one block? Can these three blues cover another block? What other colors did you use to make your block? How many colors did you use? Do these two pieces make another whole hexagon?

As students share their thinking with the whole class, have them come up to the overhead to point out where they see the different halves of the design, or to rearrange the pieces to show how the design is half-yellow.

Now show students the second example you made.

Here's another design with all different colors. Is half of this design yellow too? How can you tell?

Again give students time to work in pairs, and then bring them back to share their thinking. Listen for how students use the equivalencies they are now familiar with from their work with pattern blocks in their reasoning.②

Students might say:

"If you have two yellow blocks, you have to have enough of the other colors to make two more hexagons. Two reds can cover one block, and three blues can cover one block, so that's enough."

We're going to call this kind of design a "Half-Yellow Design" because exactly half of it is yellow. The other half is made of different colors of pattern blocks. In Math Workshop today, you can make your own Half-Yellow Design and then draw it on triangle paper, as I did.

You may want to demonstrate for students how the pattern blocks fit onto the triangle paper.

MATH WORKSHOP

② Equivalent Fractions

40 MIN

In this Math Workshop, students should finish Assessment: Many Ways to Make a Share (*Student Activity Book* page 23), including the challenge problems if they choose to do them, and make at least one Half-Yellow Design. They also may play another round of the *Fraction Cookie* game if they finish early.

You may find that for some students, the Half-Yellow activity presents too great a challenge. These students may still need to solidify their understanding of fractions when the whole remains the same size. Work with these students individually to help them complete one design, or pair them with another student to complete a design together. After they have done so, suggest that they move on to the other activities. This activity is intended as an introduction to the idea that the size of the fraction changes as the size of the whole changes. This idea is a major emphasis in the Grade 4 fraction work, and not something every student is expected to master at this point in Grade 3.

During this Math Workshop, you will also continue to observe students for the assessment that was begun in the last session.

②A Half-Yellow Designs

INDIVIDUALS   PAIRS

Working alone or with a partner, students use pattern blocks to make a design that is half-yellow. They draw and color their design on *Student Activity Book* page 25, which matches the size of the pattern blocks. Have Triangle Paper (M18) available for students who are ready to create more Half-Yellow Designs.

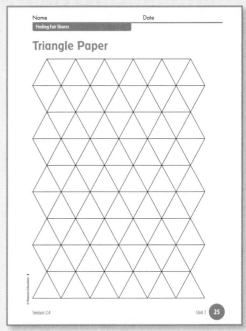

▲ Student Activity Book, p. 25;
Resource Masters, M18; T93

ONGOING ASSESSMENT: Observing Students at Work

Students construct pattern block designs in which exactly half the area is yellow.

- **Can students use their knowledge of the equivalencies of halves, thirds, and sixths to a whole to create designs that are half-yellow and half a combination of other colors?** (For example, they construct a hexagon with 1 red, 1 blue, and 1 green and then make a design with those blocks and 1 yellow; or they create a design with 2 reds, 3 blues, 6 greens, and 3 yellows.)

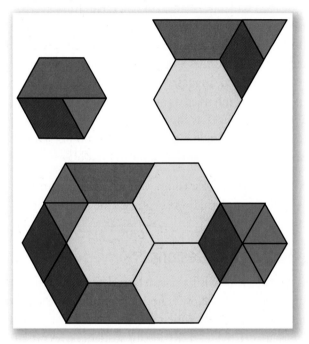

While students are making their designs, ask about their strategies with questions such as these:

- How do you know that exactly half your design is yellow?

- How did you decide which blocks to use?

- What fraction of the design is not yellow?

Also engage students in considering how the size of a fractional part is determined by its relationship to the whole.

- [Gil] is saying that in his design, $\frac{1}{2}$ the design is two yellow hexagons. [Becky], in your design, you have three yellow hexagons, and you're saying that's $\frac{1}{2}$ of the design. Why does your $\frac{1}{2}$ looks bigger than [Gil's] half? Can $\frac{1}{2}$ be two yellow hexagons sometimes and three yellow hexagons at other times?

DIFFERENTIATION: Supporting the Range of Learners

Intervention Some students may need to choose the blocks they will use in their design first and then make the design. If they understand that each hexagon will have to be matched with a set of pieces that together equal a hexagon, they can make a pile or tower of hexagons and match each hexagon with a hexagon made from green, red, and blue pattern blocks. Then, when they have their set of pieces, they can make their design.

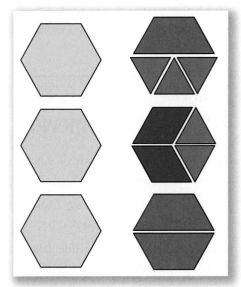

Extension Students who easily make designs that are half-yellow and can demonstrate their knowledge of pattern block equivalencies can take on the challenge of creating designs that are one fourth or one third yellow.

- -

2B Assessment: Many Ways to Make a Share

INDIVIDUALS   PAIRS

For complete details about this assessment, see Session 2.3, pages 77–79.

- -

2C The *Fraction Cookie* Game

PAIRS

For complete details about this activity, see Session 2.2, pages 70–71. Additionally, you may wish to consider the following notes.

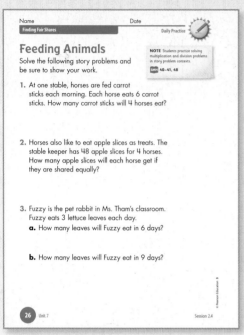

▲ **Student Activity Book, p. 26**

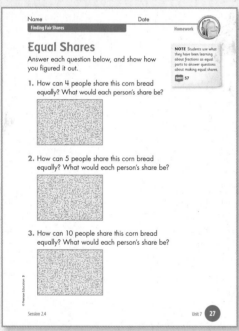

▲ **Student Activity Book, p. 27**

DIFFERENTIATION: Supporting the Range of Learners

Extension Some students may be ready for the advanced variation of the game. In the advanced game, *Adding and Subtracting Fraction Cookies,* players roll two cubes of one color and a third cube of a different color. They add the amounts on the first two cubes and then subtract the amount on the third cube from their cookie collections. In this version of the game, players start with two whole hexagon cookies so that they will not run out when they subtract. The first player to get four cookies (or another number students can decide on) wins. See the directions for this variation on the *Fraction Cookie* game (M14–M15).

SESSION FOLLOW-UP

③ Daily Practice and Homework

Daily Practice: For ongoing review, have students complete *Student Activity Book* page 26.

Homework: On *Student Activity Book* page 27, students divide rectangles into different fractional parts.

Student Math Handbook: Students and families may use *Student Math Handbook* pages 63, 64 and G11–G12 for reference and review. See pages 124–127 in the back of this unit.

Mathematical Emphases

Rational Numbers Understanding the meaning of fractions (halves, fourths, eighths, thirds, sixths) and decimal fractions (0.50, 0.25) as equal parts of a whole (an object, an area, a set of objects)

Math Focus Points

◆ Identifying equivalent fractions and decimals for values involving halves and fourths (e.g., $\frac{1}{2} = 0.50$, $\frac{1}{4} = 0.25$, $2\frac{1}{2} = 2.5$)

◆ Reading, writing, and interpreting the meaning of the decimal numbers 0.50, 0.25, and numbers greater than 1 with these decimal portions, such as 2.5 and 2.25

Introduction to Decimals

	Student Activity Book	Student Math Handbook	Professional Development: Read Ahead of Time	
SESSION 3.1 p. 90				
Sharing Money Students solve problems with items that can be split into fractional parts and ones that cannot. They discuss the meaning of the decimal notation 0.25. They solve problems involving the decimal notation for amounts of money.	29–32	65		
SESSION 3.2 p. 96				
Decimals on a Calculator Students discuss the meaning of equivalent fraction and decimal notation, using problems about dividing amounts of money (e.g., $\frac{1}{4}$ of a dollar equals 0.25). They examine the relationship between fractions and decimals by solving problems with and without a calculator.	30, 33–37	65	• **Dialogue Box:** Sharing Dollars, p. 123	
SESSION 3.3 p. 103				
Fractions and Decimals That Are Equal Students continue comparing the value of landmark decimals and fractions.	33–35, 39	65		
SESSION 3.4 p. 106				
End-of-Unit Assessment Students solve two problems to assess whether they can identify fractional parts of a whole and fractions of a group of objects, and whether they can use their knowledge of equivalencies to determine whether $\frac{1}{3} + \frac{2}{4}$ is equal to 1.	40	57, 58–59, 63, 64	• **Teacher Note:** End-of-Unit Assessment, p. 115	

Materials to Gather	Materials to Prepare
• **Calculators** (1 per pair) • **Connecting cubes** (as needed) • **Pennies, coin sets, paper bills**	• **M11, Small Brownies** Make copies for use throughout the investigation. (as needed)
• **M11, Small Brownies** (from Session 3.1; as needed) • **Calculators** (1 per pair) • **Connecting cubes** (as needed)	
• **M11, Small Brownies** (from Session 3.1; as needed) • **Connecting cubes** (as needed)	
• **Students' Fraction Sets** (from Sessions 1.2 and 1.3; as needed) • **Pattern blocks** (as needed)	• **M19, End-of-Unit Assessment** Make copies.

Sharing Money

Math Focus Points

◈ Identifying equivalent fractions and decimals for values involving halves and fourths (e.g., $\frac{1}{2} = 0.50$, $\frac{1}{4} = 0.25$, $2\frac{1}{2} = 2.5$)

Vocabulary

decimal point
decimal

Today's Plan			Materials
ACTIVITY ❶ **Can We Split It?**	20 MIN	PAIRS	• *Student Activity Book*, p. 29 • M11 (as needed)* • Calculators; connecting cubes (as needed)
DISCUSSION ❷ **Can We Split It?**	15 MIN	CLASS	
ACTIVITY ❸ **Sharing Dollars**	25 MIN	PAIRS	• *Student Activity Book*, p. 30 • Pennies; coin sets; paper bills
SESSION FOLLOW-UP ❹ **Daily Practice and Homework**			• *Student Activity Book*, pp. 31–32 • *Student Math Handbook*, p. 65

*See *Materials to Prepare,* p. 89.

Ten-Minute Math

What Time Is It?   Write 11:58 on the board and ask students to show the time on their clocks. Then ask students:

• If I put a loaf of bread in the oven at 11:58 and baked it for 47 minutes, what time will it be when I take it out of the oven?

In pairs, students share ideas about what time they think it will be and show the new time on their clocks. As a class, make sure that students can "cross over" the hour. Ask students a similar question, starting with 7:11 as the starting time and 59 minutes for duration.

ACTIVITY

1 Can We Split It?

20 MIN   PAIRS

These three sessions are an introduction to decimals. Students learn to recognize decimal notation for some of the landmark fractions they know (for example, $\frac{1}{4}$ and $\frac{1}{2}$) and use their knowledge of money to think through why $0.25 = \frac{1}{4}$ and $0.50 = \frac{1}{2}$. They work explicitly with the place value of decimals in Grade 4.

Over the past few days we have been imagining sharing brownies and cookies. Let's think about other things we can share equally between two friends. Could we share an apple? A balloon? A dollar?

List several items on the board—some that can be cut into fractional parts and some that cannot (e.g., balloons cannot be cut apart, so a balloon cannot be shared equally between two people, but a brownie can be). Allow students a few minutes to talk with a partner about which things can be split into fractional parts and which things cannot.

Bring students together to record their ideas on the board. Write students' ideas in two lists, one titled "Things We Can Split" and the other titled "Things We Cannot Split." Classrooms that did this activity have included the following on their lists. (You or your students may or may not agree with all of them!)❶

Things We Can Split:	Things We Cannot Split:
apples/fruit	balloons
brownies/cookies	people/hair
paper	oceans
books	clothes
land	planets
pizza	scissors
string	light bulbs
tape	
beverages	

Have students work on *Student Activity Book* page 29 in pairs, and have each student write an answer on his or her own page. Allow about 15 minutes for students to work on these problems before you bring them together for the following discussion.

Math Note

❶ **Mathematics and the Real World** On *Student Activity Book* page 29, students split nine things among four people. Using mathematical reasoning, nine can be divided by four with the result expressed as $2\frac{1}{4}$, 2.25, or 2 R1. In real division situations, nine things cannot always be equally divided into four parts or four groups. For example, a balloon cannot be split into pieces—or, if it is, it can no longer function properly as a balloon. Similarly, nine cents cannot be equally split among four people because we do not have any coin denominations smaller than one cent. In this session, students consider both how nine objects can or cannot be divided equally in several situations and also the different ways in which the result of the division can be expressed.

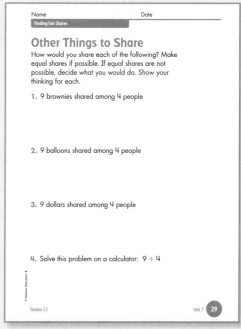

▲ **Student Activity Book, p. 29**

Encourage students to use objects such as cubes or pictures to help them share these items. They also solve one problem on the calculator.

ONGOING ASSESSMENT: Observing Students at Work

Students solve three different problems, which involve dividing nine objects among four people.

- **Can students determine which items can be split and which cannot?** Can they make reasonable decisions about how to share (e.g., one person gets four balloons and the other gets five, or there is one balloon left over)?

- **Can students accurately divide an amount of money?**

- **When students see 2.25 on the calculator, what do they think this number means?** Is this notation familiar or unfamiliar?

DISCUSSION

15 MIN   CLASS

2 Can We Split It?

Math Focus Points for Discussion

◆ Identifying equivalent fractions and decimals for values involving halves and fourths (e.g., $\frac{1}{2} = 0.50$, $\frac{1}{4} = 0.25$, $2\frac{1}{2} = 2.5$)

List the answers to each problem on the board (Problem 1: $2\frac{1}{4}$; Problem 2: 2 with one left over or 3 for one person, 2 for the others; Problem 3: 2 dollars and a quarter or \$2.25; Problem 4: 2.25).

How were your answers different when you solved each of these problems?

There are several things that students may notice.

- Balloons cannot be split, so the answer of $2\frac{1}{4}$ does not make sense (each person can have two balloons and then there will be one left over, or they do not get equal numbers).

- Two dollars and twenty-five cents is written the same way as the answer to $9 \div 4$ on a calculator (2.25, or with money notation, \$2.25).

- $\frac{1}{4}$ of a brownie can also be written as 0.25.

Collect students' ideas, and ask questions that probe their understanding of the notation 0.25 and how it is related to $0.25 and to $\frac{1}{4}$. ❷

The class discusses fractions and decimals that are equivalent.

Math Note

❷ **Division Notation** In Unit 5, *Equal Groups*, students learned to recognize and use two division symbols, $\div$ and $\overline{)\,}$. As they are writing division equations here, make sure that students use the signs correctly. Some students may use the equal sign incorrectly to show some of their solutions. For example, students may solve Problem 2, nine balloons shared among four people, by saying that each person gets two balloons and the other balloon is given away. However, although their solution is "two balloons for each person," it is not correct to write $9 \div 4 = 2$ because $9 \div 4$ is not equivalent to 2. Students can write their solutions in words or write one answer to $9 \div 4$ is 2 R1. Another solution may be that three people each get two balloons and the fourth person gets three balloons. Again, it is not correct to write $9 \div 4 = 2 + 2 + 2 + 3$, but this solution can be expressed in words.

When you divided 9 by 4 on the calculator, you got this number: 2.25. Who knows what this number means?

Students may know that $0.25 means 25 cents but may be unsure what 0.25 means on the calculator. Write the following on the board:

$$2\tfrac{1}{4} = 2.25$$

These two numbers are equal. This dot that looks like a period is called a decimal point. Numbers that include a decimal point show a part of the number that is less than one. The part of the number that is on the right side of the decimal point or that comes after the decimal point is a part of a whole. In this case, 0.25 is equal to one fourth, so 2.25 means two whole things, such as two brownies, plus $\frac{1}{4}$ of a brownie. Is there anything you know that could help you explain why 0.25 is the same amount as $\frac{1}{4}$?

If no student brings up money, ask them what they know about 25 cents—why is the coin that is worth 25 cents called a quarter? Help students think about what $2.25 means: two whole dollars and a fourth of a dollar. However, do not expect that most students will understand the meaning of 0.25 at the end of this session. You will return to this discussion during the next two sessions.

Teaching Note

❸ **Familiarity with Money** Students solved problems involving money in *Trading Stickers, Combining Coins* (Unit 1) and *Collections and Travel Stories* (Unit 3) and should be familiar with all coins. If some are not as familiar as needed, provide time outside of math class for them to explore the coins, and how many of each coin equal one dollar.

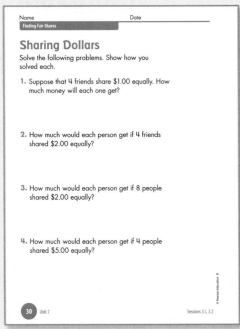

▲ **Student Activity Book, p. 30**

This is also a good time to review notation for money. Highlight for the class some different ways to write money, such as $1.00, $1.25, $0.25 (or $.25) and 25¢. Explain that we do not use a decimal point and ¢ together. To write 25 cents, we write either $0.25, which means one quarter or one fourth of a dollar, or we write 25¢. Similarly, $0.75 means three fourths or three quarters of a dollar.

Numbers that include a decimal point are called decimals. Decimal numbers are another way to write parts of wholes. We'll be studying some decimals that are a different way to write some of the fractions you know, such as $\frac{1}{2}$ and $\frac{1}{4}$. You will see a decimal instead of a fraction on most calculators. As we work for the next few days we are going to find ways to write a few fractions as decimals. So far we have found one.

Write "$\frac{1}{4} = 0.25$" on the board.

Are there any other decimals you know?❸

ACTIVITY

❸ Sharing Dollars

25 MIN   PAIRS

Students solve four problems on *Student Activity Book* page 30.

Encourage all students to use play money or draw pictures to show their solutions for each problem. They will be using calculators to solve these same problems in the next session, so they should have their work available then.

Students' representations of sharing money may look like the following:

How much would each person get if eight people shared $2.00 equally?

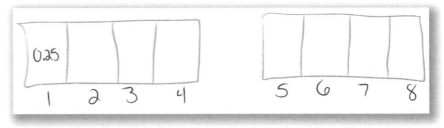

Students might say:

"I traded in my dollars for quarters—four quarters for each dollar. I passed out a quarter for each person. Each person got one quarter."

As students work, check to see whether they need reminders about how to notate amounts of money.

ONGOING ASSESSMENT: Observing Students at Work

Students share amounts of money among different numbers of people.

- **Can students accurately share each amount of money?** Do they use pictures or play money? Do they reason about the equivalencies they know (e.g., I know that four quarters make a dollar, so eight quarters would make two dollars)?

- **Can students notate amounts of money?** Can they write $0.25 or 25¢?

SESSION FOLLOW-UP
Daily Practice and Homework

 Daily Practice: For ongoing review, have students complete *Student Activity Book* page 31.

 Homework: On *Student Activity Book* page 32, students identify different combinations of fractions that equal one whole hexagon.

 Student Math Handbook: Students and families may use *Student Math Handbook* page 65 for reference and review. See pages 124–127 in the back of this unit.

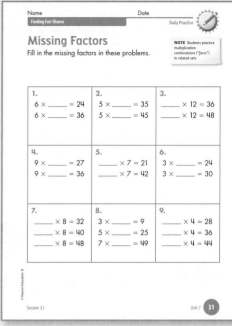

▲ Student Activity Book, p. 31

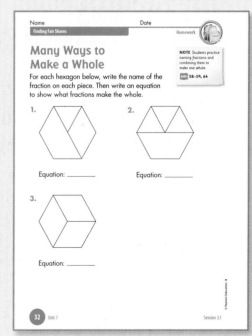

▲ Student Activity Book, p. 32

Decimals on a Calculator

Math Focus Points

◆ Identifying equivalent fractions and decimals for values involving halves and fourths (e.g., $\frac{1}{2} = 0.50$, $\frac{1}{4} = 0.25$, $2\frac{1}{2} = 2.5$)

◆ Reading, writing, and interpreting the meaning of the decimal numbers 0.50, 0.25, and numbers greater than 1 with these decimal portions, such as 2.5 and 2.25

Today's Plan		Materials
DISCUSSION ① **Fractions and Decimals**	20 MIN CLASS	• *Student Activity Book,* p. 30 (from Session 3.1) • Calculators
MATH WORKSHOP ② **Sharing with Fractions and Decimals** ②A Sharing With and Without a Calculator ②B My Own Sharing Problems	40 MIN	2A • *Student Activity Book,* pp. 33–34 2B • *Student Activity Book,* p. 35 • M11 (from Session 3.1; as needed) • Connecting cubes
SESSION FOLLOW-UP ③ **Daily Practice and Homework**		• *Student Activity Book,* pp. 36–37 • *Student Math Handbook,* p. 65

Ten-Minute Math

What Time Is It? **Tell students the following story:**

• I walked to soccer practice. I left my house at 3:26 and arrived at the field at 3:53. How long did it take me to walk to the field?

In pairs, students share their ideas. Collect ideas and focus on strategies in which students count the interval by 5s, or other chunks (such as 30 minutes from 3:26–3:56, minus 3 minutes from 30 makes 27 minutes total). Ask additional similar questions using 11:37 as the starting time and 12:16 as the ending time.

DISCUSSION
Fractions and Decimals

20 MIN CLASS

Math Focus Points for Discussion

◆ Identifying equivalent fractions and decimals for values involving halves and fourths (e.g., $\frac{1}{2} = 0.50$, $\frac{1}{4} = 0.25$, $2\frac{1}{2} = 2.5$)

Return students' attention to the problems they solved at the end of the last session on *Student Activity Book* page 30.

Solve these problems again, but this time use a calculator. Notice the answer you get on the calculator.

Students need their work from the previous session and a calculator (one per pair). Students work on each problem, experimenting with the calculators until they get the answers they expect.❶ ❷

Choose either Problem 1 or Problem 3 to use as an example, and list the solutions students found with and without a calculator on the board. Ask them how they wrote their answer or whether they can think of other ways to write the answer. For example, for Problem 3, sharing two dollars among eight people equally, students may offer the following:

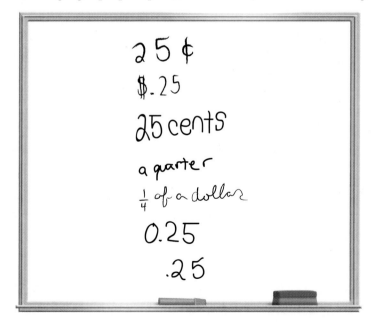

Then ask students about the connections between the different ways of expressing this quantity. If students have not offered some of the ways listed above, ask whether those not mentioned represent the same quantity.

Math Note

❸ **Saying and Writing Decimals** Because students are not yet learning about tenths and hundredths (they will study these ideas in Grade 4), say decimals in this way: 0.25 is "point two five," and 3.5 is "three point five." Students will also notice the 0 on the calculator for 0.25 and 0.5. Ask them what they think this 0 means. Contrast 0.25 with 2.25, and compare these numbers with $\frac{1}{4}$ and $2\frac{1}{4}$. Help students understand that the 0 to the left of the decimal point means 0 whole numbers.

[Keisha] wrote 25¢. What does this mean? Do you see another way of writing the answer that is like 25¢ in some ways? [Oscar], you think "$0.25" is like "25¢." How are they alike? How are they different? Do you see a way that seems quite different to you than "25¢"? How is it different? Is it also like "25¢" in some ways? I don't think anyone wrote "$\frac{1}{4}$ of a dollar." Could this be a correct answer, too? Why or why not?

Make sure that you discuss "$\frac{1}{4}$ of a dollar" and "a quarter."

Why do you think the coin that is worth 25 cents is called a quarter?

This discussion will help you assess what notations are meaningful to your students and whether they see how some of these are equivalent ways of representing the same amount. It also helps students think about 25 cents as a fourth, or a quarter, of a dollar. When you think students have contributed most of what they understand, focus on the answer students got on the calculator, 0.25.

When you used the calculator, you got 0.25 as an answer. Does this make sense to you? What do you think it means? If "0.25" is a part of a whole, what part is it? Is it like any fraction that you know? Why do you think so?❸

Students might say:

"0.25 is like 25 cents. You write it almost the same way if you use the dollar sign."

"25 fits into 100 four times, so it is a fourth of 100. So $\frac{1}{4}$ and 0.25 are the same amount."

"0.25 is one quarter. If you add four quarters together, you get $1.00. So $\frac{1}{4}$ and 0.25 are the same."

Now discuss Problem 2 in the same way. Again, ask for students' ways of recording their answer, and add any additional ways that came up in the discussion of the third problem. Then compare their answers with the calculator answer.

Students will notice that the calculator shows $\frac{1}{2}$ as 0.5. They may wonder why the equivalent of 50 cents looks like 0.5 on the calculator instead of 0.50. It is also confusing that a smaller number, 0.25 ($\frac{1}{4}$), has two digits after the decimal point and 0.5 has only one. If students do not mention this, raise it yourself.

The smaller fraction, one fourth, has two numbers (digits) after the decimal point—0.25. But one half only has one number—0.5. Why do you think that is?

After accepting students' ideas, explain that 0.5 and 0.50 both mean one half. Explain that the calculator shows the amount in the shortest way possible as 0.5.

Record on the board the equivalencies you talked about in this discussion.

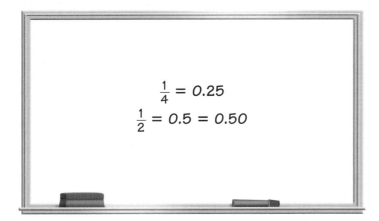

$$\frac{1}{4} = 0.25$$
$$\frac{1}{2} = 0.5 = 0.50$$

Students will have many more opportunities to continue to develop an understanding of the relationship between fractions, decimals and division. It is important here for students to begin to recognize the connection between decimal notation for money and the fraction of 100 that this notation represents (i.e., $0.25 = \frac{1}{4}$ because $\frac{1}{4}$ of 100 is 25, and $0.50 = \frac{1}{2}$ because $\frac{1}{2}$ of 100 is 50).❹

MATH WORKSHOP

② Sharing with Fractions and Decimals

40 MIN

Students continue to share items (money and brownies) and record their answers in both fractions and decimals. They use a calculator to find the decimal notation for equal shares and consider how different fraction and decimal notations represent the same quantity.

Professional Development

❹ **Dialogue Box:** Sharing Dollars, p. 123

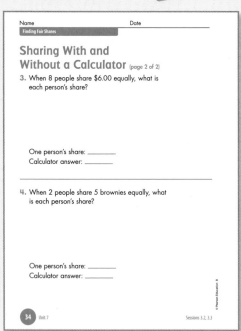

Name _____ Date _____

Finding Fair Shares

Sharing With and Without a Calculator (page 1 of 2)

Solve each of the problems below. First solve the problem without using a calculator and show how you figured it out. Then solve it with a calculator.

1. When 2 people share $3.00 equally, what is each person's share?

One person's share: _____
Calculator answer: _____

2. When 4 people share $3.00 equally, what is each person's share?

One person's share: _____
Calculator answer: _____

Sessions 3.2, 3.3   Unit 7   33

▲ **Student Activity Book, p. 33** PORTFOLIO

Name _____ Date _____

Finding Fair Shares

Sharing With and Without a Calculator (page 2 of 2)

3. When 8 people share $6.00 equally, what is each person's share?

One person's share: _____
Calculator answer: _____

4. When 2 people share 5 brownies equally, what is each person's share?

One person's share: _____
Calculator answer: _____

34   Unit 7   Sessions 3.2, 3.3

▲ **Student Activity Book, p. 34** PORTFOLIO

2A Sharing With and Without a Calculator

PAIRS

Students work on *Student Activity Book* pages 33–34 with a partner. These pages present some problems similar to ones students solved in Investigations 1 and 2, although now the context is money.

Students solve each problem mentally or with a drawing. They then find an answer with a calculator in order to see decimal notation equivalent to their other ways of representing the solution.

Students practice solving sharing problems with and without a calculator.

ONGOING ASSESSMENT: Observing Students at Work

Students divide money into equal amounts and represent their answers in decimals.

- **Can students equally share amounts of money?** Can they split a remaining dollar into equal amounts in cents?

- **Do students use coins and deal them out or do they use their knowledge of money equivalencies to determine how much each person will get** (e.g., there are four quarters in a dollar so I know that four people sharing two dollars will get two quarters— or 50 cents—each)?

- **Can students identify common fraction and decimal equivalents (e.g., $0.5 = \frac{1}{2}$ and $0.25 = \frac{1}{4}$)?**

DIFFERENTIATION: Supporting the Range of Learners

Intervention If students are having difficulty sharing dollars, encourage them to use relationships that they already know about 100 (e.g., $4 \times 25 = 100$, 4 quarters = one dollar). Using play money, they can trade in a dollar for other coins. Make sure that students know and understand how many quarters, dimes, and nickels are in a dollar. You may want to suggest that students begin with sharing one dollar among different numbers of people.

Extension If some students need more of a challenge, ask them to try sharing an amount of money that is not a multiple of one dollar; for example, $4.50 shared equally among six people.

2B My Own Sharing Problems

INDIVIDUALS   PAIRS

On *Student Activity Book* page 35, students make up problems in which they figure out a quantity and a number of equal shares that will result in shares of $\frac{1}{2}$, $\frac{1}{4}$, and $\frac{3}{4}$.

These problems may be challenging for some students, but solving them helps develop flexibility with parts, wholes, and fraction equivalents. After students make up their problems, they should share and check them with a partner. Cubes, brownie rectangles, and drawing materials should be made available to all students.

ONGOING ASSESSMENT: Observing Students at Work

Students determine a quantity and the number of equal shares that will result in a certain size share.

- **Do students use reasoning about fraction relationships to determine the quantity and number of shares** (e.g., I know that four fourths make one whole, so if four people share one thing, each will get $\frac{1}{4}$, and if eight people share two things, each will get $\frac{1}{4}$)?

- **Do students use money or cut up rectangles to determine the total and number of shares?** If so, do they use trial and error, or do they use knowledge of fractions?

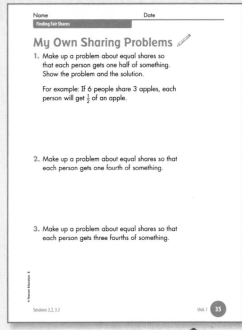

▲ Student Activity Book, p. 35

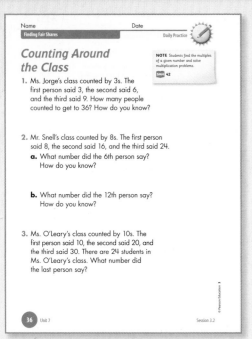

▲ Student Activity Book, p. 36

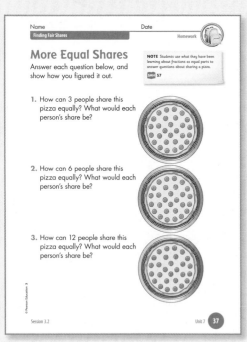

▲ Student Activity Book, p. 37

DIFFERENTIATION: Supporting the Range of Learners

Intervention These problems can be challenging if students are still struggling with how to share objects equally. These students may benefit from first solving Sharing With and Without a Calculator problems and perhaps additional problems that you create. This will help students gain experience before moving on to *Student Activity Book* page 35.

Extension Students can make up more of these kinds of problems and attempt to challenge their peers. You can ask them to make up problems in which each person has $\frac{2}{3}$, $\frac{3}{6}$, or $\frac{3}{4}$ of a whole.

SESSION FOLLOW-UP
3 Daily Practice and Homework

 Daily Practice: For ongoing review, have students complete *Student Activity Book* page 36.

 Homework: Students create equal shares for different numbers of people sharing a pizza on *Student Activity Book* page 37.

 Student Math Handbook: Students and families may use *Student Math Handbook* page 65 for reference and review. See pages 124–127 in the back of this unit.

Fractions and Decimals That Are Equal

Math Focus Points

◆ Identifying equivalent fractions and decimals for values involving halves and fourths (e.g., $\frac{1}{2} = 0.50$, $\frac{1}{4} = 0.25$, $2\frac{1}{2} = 2.5$)

◆ Reading, writing, and interpreting the meaning of the decimal numbers 0.50, 0.25, and numbers greater than 1 with these decimal portions, such as 2.5 and 2.25

Today's Plan		Materials
MATH WORKSHOP **① Sharing with Fractions and Decimals** **①A Sharing With and Without a Calculator** **①B My Own Sharing Problems**	40 MIN	**①A** • *Student Activity Book,* pp. 33–34 **①B** • *Student Activity Book,* p. 35 • M11 (from Session 3.1; as needed) • Connecting cubes
DISCUSSION **② Finding Fraction and Decimal Equivalents**	20 MIN CLASS PAIRS	
SESSION FOLLOW-UP **③ Daily Practice**		• *Student Activity Book,* p. 39 • *Student Math Handbook,* p. 65

Ten-Minute Math

What Time Is It? Tell students the following story:

• The school assembly started at 11:42 and ended at 12:13. How long was the assembly?

In pairs, students share their ideas. Collect ideas and focus on strategies in which students count the interval by 5s, or other chunks (such as 20 minutes from 11:42–12:02, plus 11 minutes more to 12:13 makes 31 minutes total). Ask additional similar questions using 9:02 as the starting time and 9:39 as the ending time.

MATH WORKSHOP

1 Sharing with Fractions and Decimals

40 MIN

Students continue finding fraction and decimal equivalents. The second activity, My Own Sharing Problems, is very engaging for many students. You may want to encourage students to write their own problems to share with a partner.

1A Sharing With and Without a Calculator

PAIRS

For complete details about this activity, see Session 3.2, page 100.

1B My Own Sharing Problems

INDIVIDUALS PAIRS

For complete details about this activity, see Session 3.2, page 101.

DISCUSSION

2 Finding Fraction and Decimal Equivalents

20 MIN CLASS PAIRS

Math Focus Points for Discussion

◆ Identifying equivalent fractions and decimals for values involving halves and fourths (e.g., $\frac{1}{2} = 0.50$, $\frac{1}{4} = 0.25$, $2\frac{1}{2} = 2.5$)

Begin by asking students about what fractions and decimal equivalents they know.

I know that we have been working with these new numbers called *decimals* for only a couple of days, but I bet you know more decimal and fraction equivalents than you think you do. We know now that $\frac{1}{2} = 0.50$. Do you know any other fractions that are equal to $\frac{1}{2}$?

On chart paper or the board, begin a list of fraction and decimal equivalents. Group the problems by each fraction. As students share fractions that are equivalent to $\frac{1}{2}$, encourage them to use the list of equivalent fractions or use brownies or pattern blocks to find more.

Fractions and Decimals		
$\frac{1}{2} = 0.5$	$\frac{1}{4} = 0.25$	$\frac{3}{4} = 0.75$
$\frac{2}{4} = 0.5$	$\frac{2}{8} = 0.25$	
$\frac{3}{6} = 0.5$		

Some students may notice that all of the fractions that equal 0.50 have the same relationship between the numerator and the denominator; that is, the denominator is twice as big as the numerator (e.g., $\frac{1}{2}$, $\frac{2}{4}$, $\frac{3}{6}$). If no one brings this up, ask about it.

Does anyone notice a pattern in the fractions that all equal 0.50? Can anyone find a pattern? Look carefully at the numerator and the denominator.

Collect some responses. Students will notice that the denominator is twice the numerator in each case.

Take out your calculators. If you divide the numerator by the denominator in all these examples, what do you get?

Students may or may not know that fractions are a way to notate division. Let students know that $\frac{1}{2}$ is another way to write one divided by two. Allow students to explore carrying out these divisions for fractions equivalent to $\frac{1}{2}$ and then ask them to list and then try dividing fraction equivalents for 0.25.

You can also ask about 0.75, 1.25 or 1.5, if you think your students are ready to consider these values.

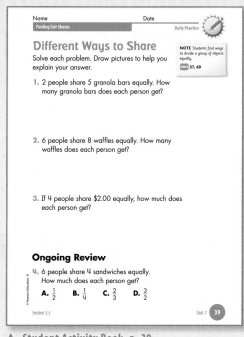

▲ **Student Activity Book, p. 39**

SESSION FOLLOW-UP
3 Daily Practice

 Daily Practice: For reinforcement of this unit's content, have students complete *Student Activity Book* page 39.

 Student Math Handbook: Students and families may use *Student Math Handbook* page 65 for reference and review. See pages 124–127 in the back of this unit.

End-of-Unit Assessment

Math Focus Points

- Finding equal parts of a whole and naming them with fractions
- Dividing an area into equal parts
- Using representations to combine fractions that sum to 1 (e.g., $\frac{1}{4} + \frac{3}{4} = 1, \frac{1}{3} + \frac{1}{3} + \frac{1}{3} = 1; \frac{1}{2} + \frac{1}{4} + \frac{1}{4} = 1$)
- Identifying equivalent fractional parts

Today's Plan	Materials
ASSESSMENT ACTIVITY **1** **End-of-Unit Assessment** ✔ 🕐 👤 60 MIN INDIVIDUALS	• M19* • Students' Fraction Sets (from Sessions 1.2 and 1.3; as needed); pattern blocks (as needed)
SESSION FOLLOW-UP **2** **Daily Practice**	• *Student Activity Book,* p. 40 • *Student Math Handbook,* pp. 57, 58–59, 63, 64

*See *Materials to Prepare,* p. 89.

Ten-Minute Math

What Time Is It? **Tell students the following story:**

- The movie started at 8:45 and ended at 10:05. How long was the movie?

In pairs, students share their ideas. Collect ideas and focus on strategies in which students count by chunks (such as 15 minutes from 8:45–9:00, plus 1 hour to 10:00, and 5 minutes more to 10:05 makes 1 hour and 20 minutes total). Ask additional similar questions using 9:02 as the starting time and 10:39 as the ending time.

ASSESSMENT ACTIVITY

End-of-Unit Assessment

60 MIN INDIVIDUALS

On End-of-Unit Assessment (M19), students work individually to solve two assessment problems.❶ These problems address the following benchmarks for the unit.

Benchmark 1: Divide a single whole or a quantity into equal parts, and name those parts as fractions or mixed numbers.

Benchmark 2: Identify equivalent fractions (e.g., $\frac{3}{6} = \frac{1}{2}$ and $\frac{1}{3} = \frac{2}{6}$).

Benchmark 3: Find combinations of fractions that are equal to one and to other fractions (e.g., $\frac{3}{6} + \frac{1}{2} = 1$; $\frac{1}{6} + \frac{1}{6} = \frac{1}{3}$; and $\frac{1}{3} + \frac{1}{6} = \frac{1}{2}$).

Encourage students to use their Fraction Sets as well as pattern blocks to solve these problems. Also remind them to show their solutions clearly on their paper.❷

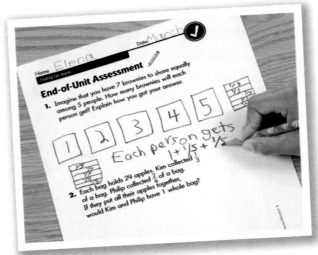

Students complete an assessment to determine their ability to divide quantities into equal parts and name the corresponding fractions.

Professional Development

❶ In the first problem, students divide 7 brownies equally among 5 people and determine how much brownie each person gets. In the second problem, students work with a bag of 24 apples. They decide whether $\frac{1}{3}$ of the apples plus $\frac{2}{4}$ of the apples is equal to the whole bag of 24 apples.

❷ **Teacher Note:** Assessment: End-of-Unit Assessment, p. 115

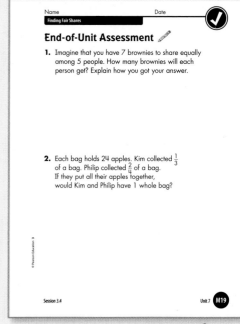

▲ **Resource Masters, M19** PORTFOLIO WRITING

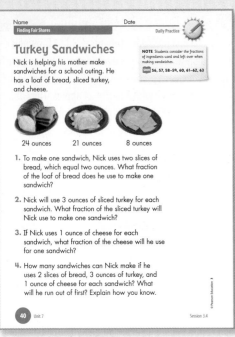

▲ Student Activity Book, p. 40

The Student Activity Book page shows:

> Name _____ Date _____
> **Finding Fair Shares**   Daily Practice
>
> ## Turkey Sandwiches
>
> Nick is helping his mother make sandwiches for a school outing. He has a loaf of bread, sliced turkey, and cheese.
>
> **NOTE** Students consider the fractions of ingredients used and left over when making sandwiches.
> **SMH** 56, 57, 58–59, 60, 61–62, 63
>
> 24 ounces   21 ounces   8 ounces
>
> 1. To make one sandwich, Nick uses two slices of bread, which equal two ounces. What fraction of the loaf of bread does he use to make one sandwich?
>
> 2. Nick will use 3 ounces of sliced turkey for each sandwich. What fraction of the sliced turkey will Nick use to make one sandwich?
>
> 3. If Nick uses 1 ounce of cheese for each sandwich, what fraction of the cheese will he use for one sandwich?
>
> 4. How many sandwiches can Nick make if he uses 2 slices of bread, 3 ounces of turkey, and 1 ounce of cheese for each sandwich? What will he run out of first? Explain how you know.
>
> 40   Unit 7   Session 3.4

ONGOING ASSESSMENT: Observing Students at Work

Students solve two assessments problems to determine whether they can identify fractions.

- **Can students divide a quantity into equal parts and accurately name each part with either a fraction or a mixed number?**

- **Can students determine fractional amounts of a group of objects?**

- **Can students reason about the result of combining two fractions with different denominators and decide whether the result would equal one whole?**

SESSION FOLLOW-UP

2 Daily Practice

 Daily Practice: For enrichment, have students complete *Student Activity Book* page 40.

 Student Math Handbook: Students and families may use *Student Math Handbook* pages 57, 58–59, 63, 64 for reference and review. See pages 124–127 in the back of this unit.

Finding Fair Shares

In Part 6 of *Implementing Investigations in Grade 3,* you will find a set of Teacher Notes that addresses topics and issues applicable to the curriculum as a whole rather than to specific curriculum units. They include the following:

Computational Fluency and Place Value

Computational Algorithms and Methods

Representations and Contexts for Mathematical Work

Foundations of Algebra in the Elementary Grades

Discussing Mathematical Ideas

Racial and Linguistic Diversity in the Classroom:
    What Does Equity Mean in Today's Math Classroom?

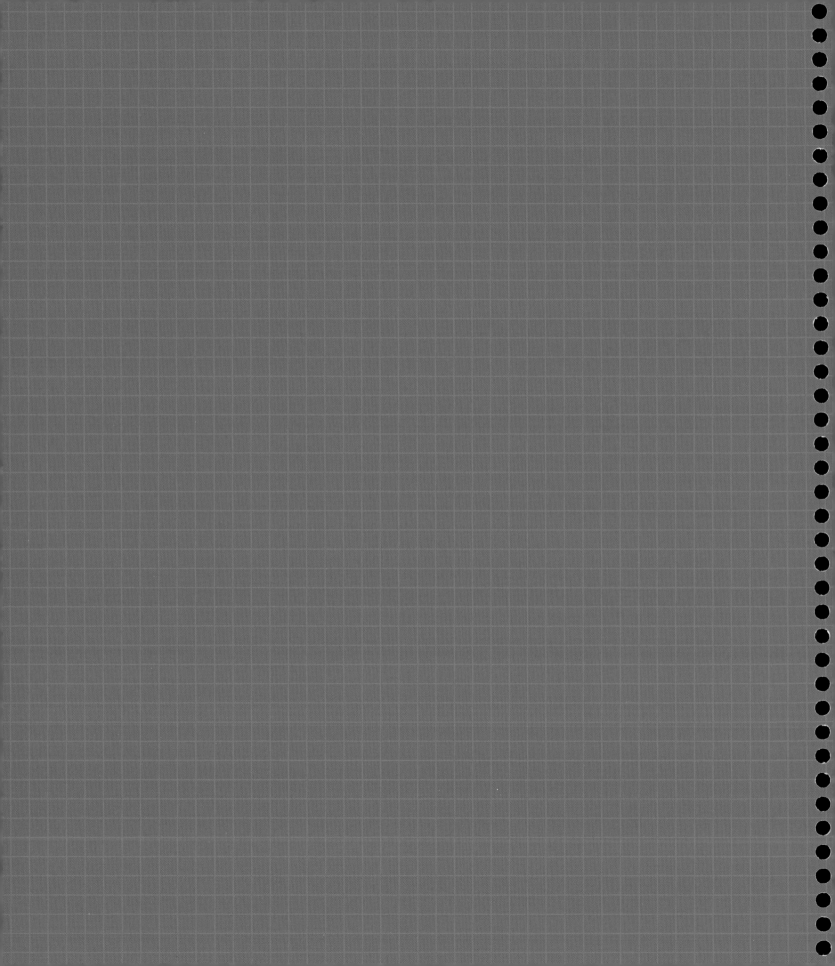

Why Are Fractions Difficult?
Developing Meaning for Fractions

Why are fractions difficult for third graders? As adults, we are used to seeing and ascribing meaning to fractions such as $\frac{1}{2}$ and $\frac{3}{4}$ in a variety of situations. Imagine how strange this notation—two whole numbers separated by a line—must look to elementary school students as they begin to dig into the meaning of fractions.

It is not surprising, then, that in trying to understand fractions, students attempt to draw on what they know from their experience with the numbers with which they are most familiar—whole numbers. For example, students may think at first that $\frac{1}{3}$ is greater than $\frac{1}{2}$ because 3 is greater than 2. There has been a great deal of research conducted regarding students' understanding of fractions, largely with middle school students. This research indicates that even in the middle grades, many students still interpret fraction notation as two separate whole numbers that are not related.

Looking at fractions as though they represent two separate whole numbers leads to misinterpretation of their meaning and an inability to assess the reasonableness of calculation results. For example, an often-cited assessment question from the National Assessment of Educational Progress (NAEP) asked students to estimate the sum of $\frac{12}{13}$ and $\frac{7}{8}$. Given four answer choices—1, 2, 19, and 21—students most often chose 19 or 21. Using whole-number addition, they added either only the numerators or only the denominators. These students were not able to think of each of these numbers as being close to 1 and thus missed the correct estimate of 2.

In order to develop meaning for fractions, students work with the context of "fair shares," in which something is shared equally. One key idea in this unit—and throughout students' study of fractions—is that a fraction represents a quantity in relation to a unit whole. Examples of unit wholes could include a single object, an area, a linear measure, or a group of objects. In this context, "$\frac{1}{2}$" means "one out of two equal parts that make up one whole."

One half of one whole is not the same quantity as one half of another whole; for example, $\frac{1}{2}$ a class of 26 is 13 students, and $\frac{1}{2}$ a class of 22 is 11 students. However, although $\frac{1}{2}$ can represent many different quantities, depending on the size of the whole, $\frac{1}{2}$ has the *same relationship* to *any* whole. It is one of the two equal parts that compose the whole. In this unit, students work with fractions in relation to a whole that is a single object ($\frac{1}{4}$ of one brownie), an area ($\frac{2}{3}$ of the surface of a hexagonal pattern block), or a group of things ($\frac{1}{4}$ of six brownies). The focus is twofold: the parts of the whole must be equal to one another, and all the parts combined must equal the whole. It is not unusual for third graders to ignore one or both of these ideas at first. For example, when dividing brownies, they may make unequal pieces (as in the first picture) or cut off part of the whole in order to make the pieces equal (as in the second picture below).

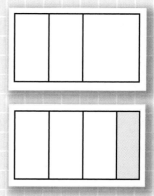

The ideas in this unit also lay the groundwork for division of a smaller number by a larger one. Students sometimes think or are told by adults, "You can't subtract a larger number from a smaller one," when of course it is quite possible to solve such a problem when you know about negative numbers ($4 - 7 = -3$). Subtracting 7 from 4 requires expanding one's knowledge of the number system to include negative numbers. Similarly, they may think, "You can't divide a smaller number by a larger one."

However, dividing 3 by 4 requires expanding one's knowledge of the number system to include rational numbers (numbers that can be represented as a division of two integers, such as $\frac{1}{2}$ or $\frac{9}{10}$). In this unit, as students work on activities such as dividing seven brownies among four people, they implicitly apply the distributive property by thinking of $7 \div 4$ as $(4 \div 4) + (3 \div 4)$. They solve the first part of the problem by assigning one brownie to each of the four people and then tackle the second part of the problem, $3 \div 4$, by solving it in a number of ways (see **Dialogue Box:** Seven Brownies, Four People, page 120).

In fact, fractions indicate division: one interpretation of $\frac{1}{2}$ is that it represents one out of two equal parts of a whole, but it also means the quantity that results from dividing one by two. In Grade 3, students are not yet thinking about fractions as an indicated division. Instead, they are learning about a fraction as a *relationship* between two numbers and how that relationship is, in turn, related to 1. In Grade 4 they will focus more on how a fraction is a *number* that always has the same relationship to 1 and will extend the use of the number line with whole numbers to fractions, mixed numbers, and decimals.

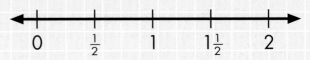

Assessment: Sharing Four Brownies

Problem 1

Benchmark addressed:

Benchmark 1: Divide a single whole or a quantity into equal parts, and name those parts as fractions or mixed numbers.

In order to meet the benchmark, students' work should show that they can:

• Divide a group of things into equal shares;

• Identify the fraction for each share.

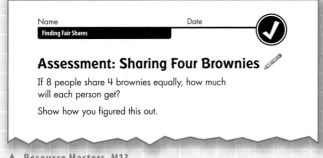

> Name _____ Date _____ ✓
> **Finding Fair Shares**
>
> **Assessment: Sharing Four Brownies** ✏
>
> If 8 people share 4 brownies equally, how much will each person get?
>
> Show how you figured this out.

▲ **Resource Masters, M13**

Meeting the Benchmark

The following are all examples of students who meet the benchmark. They understand that each of the eight people gets an equal portion of the brownies. They can also divide a brownie into fractional parts and name each piece.

Beatriz uses knowledge of multiplication, and the relationship between 4 and 8, to figure out that each person will get half a brownie.

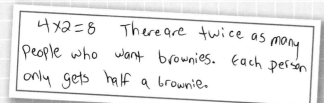

> 4×2=8 There are twice as many people who want brownies. Each person only gets half a brownie.

Beatriz's Work

Chris represents the brownies and people with rectangles and circles. He divides each brownie into two and connects it by a line to each person. He correctly identifies each share as $\frac{1}{2}$.

Chris's Work

Gina also divides each of the four brownies into pieces, but she divides them into eighths. Each person takes one eighth from each brownie. She then sees that each person gets $\frac{4}{8}$.

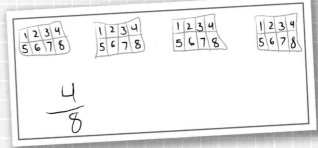

Gina's Work

Both $\frac{1}{2}$ and $\frac{4}{8}$ are correct answers and show students' ability to create eight equal shares. It would be interesting to tell Gina that another student's answer is $\frac{1}{2}$ and ask whether that could be correct as well.

Partially Meeting the Benchmark

Some students may know that each person gets an equal share of the eight brownies but cannot identify the fraction of a brownie that each person gets. For example, Oscar's drawing shows eight equal shares, but he does not identify the fraction.

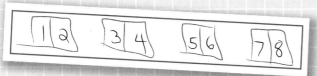

Oscar's Work

Not Meeting the Benchmark

Students who do not meet the benchmark may not divide a whole into equal pieces. In some cases, students may try to pass out one whole to each person and may not know what to do when they run out. A question for these students should be this: If eight people are sharing only four brownies, will each person get more or less than one? How do you know? Then have them use cut-out brownies or pattern blocks to distribute them equally, revising their solution as needed.

Other students may switch the numbers in the problem, solving for four people and eight brownies. If they solve this situation correctly, there is no fraction involved because each person receives two brownies. Work with these students to visualize the situation. Are they then able to solve the problem?

Visualizing Fraction Equivalencies

In this unit, students use materials and representations to build their knowledge of fraction equivalencies with halves, fourths, eighths, thirds, and sixths. Just as students build a repertoire of certain whole-number equivalencies (e.g., the single-digit addition combinations or the different ways in which 138 might be decomposed), they also build a repertoire of fraction equivalencies.

One category of fraction equivalencies students work on in this unit is individual fraction equivalents (e.g., $\frac{1}{2} = \frac{3}{6}$). These include the following:

- The set of individual fractions that equal 1 ($\frac{2}{2}, \frac{3}{3}, \frac{6}{6}, \frac{4}{4}, \frac{8}{8}$)

- The set of fractions that equal $\frac{1}{2}$ ($\frac{2}{4}, \frac{3}{6}, \frac{4}{8}$)

- Pairs of fractions in which one fraction has a numerator and denominator that are double the numerator and denominator of the other ($\frac{1}{3} = \frac{2}{6}$ and $\frac{1}{4} = \frac{2}{8}$)

A second category of fraction equivalencies is addition combinations that are equivalent to 1 or to another fraction (e.g., $\frac{1}{2} + \frac{1}{4} + \frac{1}{4} = 1$ and $\frac{1}{3} + \frac{1}{6} = \frac{1}{2}$).

Throughout this unit, students use pattern blocks, paper rectangles, and drawings to help them develop visual images of how fractions or combinations of fractions can be equal to one another. They come to understand that two halves, three thirds, and six sixths make a whole because they see the whole as "all filled up."

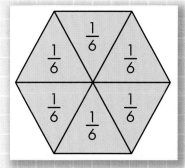

Similarly, students learn equivalents for $\frac{1}{2}$. Students notice that these fractions (e.g., $\frac{2}{4}, \frac{3}{6}, \frac{4}{8}$, and so on) are characterized by a denominator that is twice the numerator. They notice that as the size of the piece is halved, the number of pieces needed to make up the same quantity is doubled.

Equivalent fractions such as $\frac{1}{4}$ and $\frac{2}{8}$ become familiar to students as they first fold and cut, and eventually draw rectangles to represent the whole and the equal parts that are the fractions of that whole. For example, students quickly realize that when fourths are divided in half, two of the new smaller pieces equal one fourth.

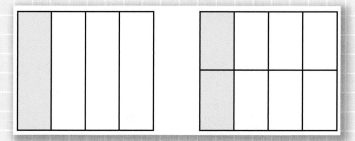

In the equal-sharing contexts of this unit, students often talk about this relationship as the size of the share being halved and the number of shares being doubled.

Students recognize that fractions with unlike denominators can be combined because they can visualize these combinations with rectangles or pattern blocks. For example, students often come away from this unit with the Fraction Fact that $\frac{1}{3} + \frac{1}{6} = \frac{1}{2}$ because they have a picture in their minds of pattern block pieces that represent $\frac{1}{3}$ and $\frac{1}{6}$.

Because they can visualize a variety of ways in which the pattern block pieces fit together to make a whole, they can use those images to visualize how the pieces fit together to make half of the whole. Without formally finding common denominators, they are using their knowledge of fraction equivalencies to solve addition problems with unlike denominators. They are also building a repertoire of known relationships.

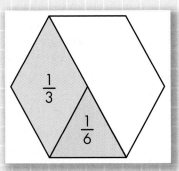

In Grades 1–3, students have been working on putting together and taking apart whole numbers. As they develop flexibility in decomposing numbers, they learn about the way our number system is structured, and they develop computational methods based on this understanding. In Grades 3–5, students engage in developing this same kind of flexibility with fractions and decimal fractions. By the end of this unit, students are using known fraction equivalencies to reason about other equivalencies (e.g., "Three sixths plus one half must be a whole because three sixths is a half, and that makes two halves"). Understanding the meaning of fractions and developing a repertoire of equivalencies are two of the key components that lay the groundwork for operations with fractions.

Teacher Note

End-of-Unit Assessment

The following describes each of the two assessment problems and provides information on interpreting and assessing student work.

Problem 1

Benchmark addressed:

Benchmark 1: Divide a single whole or a quantity into equal parts, and name those parts as fractions or mixed numbers.

In order to meet this benchmark, students' work should show that they can:

- Divide a group of things into equal shares;

- Identify the fraction or mixed number for each share.

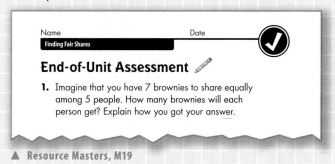

Name _____ Date _____
Finding Fair Shares

End-of-Unit Assessment

1. Imagine that you have 7 brownies to share equally among 5 people. How many brownies will each person get? Explain how you got your answer.

▲ **Resource Masters, M19**

Meeting the Benchmark

Most students who meet the benchmark draw a picture that shows how the brownies are broken up and shared equally among the people. Pictures involve faces, rectangles, and lines that connect portions of brownies with people. Look carefully to see whether the student has, in fact, created equal shares. Some work includes only pictures and some includes pictures and words that describe how the student divided the seven brownies.

Students' work must show that each person gets one whole brownie plus $\frac{2}{5}$ of a brownie. However, they may write these answers differently, including $1\frac{2}{5}$; $1 + \frac{1}{5} + \frac{1}{5}$; and $\frac{7}{5}$. All of these answers meet the benchmark.

Chiang's representation shows that she knows each portion has to be equal, and, after she has given each person one brownie, she can successfully divide each of the other two brownies into five equal pieces and identify each piece as $\frac{1}{5}$. She combines these pieces to get $1\frac{2}{5}$.

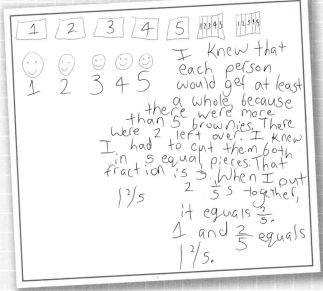

Chiang's Work

Denzel's work represents another common solution to this problem. He breaks all seven brownies into five pieces (because he is dividing them among five people). He assigns one piece from each brownie to each of the five people. He knows that when he combines all seven pieces, each share is $\frac{7}{5}$ of a brownie. This answer is correct, but it would also be interesting to ask Denzel, "Will each person get more or less than one brownie?" to find out whether he knows that $\frac{7}{5}$ is greater than one.

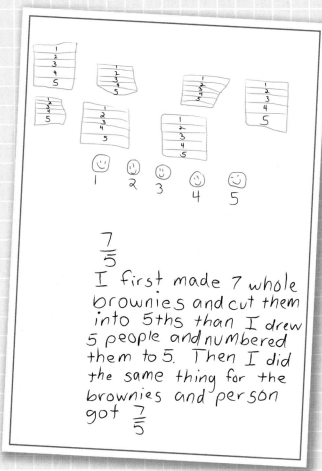

Denzel's Work

Deondra draws a picture that includes faces (for people) and rectangles (for brownies). Although there are no words to accompany her drawing, she shows that each person is connected to one whole brownie and $\frac{1}{5}$ of each of the extra two brownies. She records her answer as $1 + \frac{1}{5} + \frac{1}{5}$.

Deondra's Work

Partially Meeting the Benchmark

Some students may draw a picture that accurately represents five people equally sharing seven brownies, but may not write the amount of each share.

Ines shows a picture of each person getting one whole brownie, and the last two appear to be broken into equal pieces. Her picture is very hard to read, but when her teacher asked her about it, she explained that each brownie was cut into five equal pieces. Either she does not know how to write the answer that includes a fraction, or she has forgotten to include it. Ines should be asked to identify clearly each portion in her drawing and consider what she would name it. Ask questions such as these: "Is it more or less than one brownie? What fraction of the whole brownie are the extra pieces? Show me in your picture."

Ines's Work

Kathryn draws a picture that shows that she can divide the two extra brownies into equal pieces (and knows that it is five equal pieces), but she cannot determine what to name each portion.

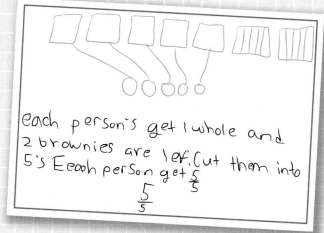

Kathryn's Work

Not Meeting the Benchmark

Students who do not meet the benchmark often solve the problem in a practical way but do not find equal shares of the seven brownies. They are also not able to use fractions or mixed numbers correctly to represent a quantity.

Philip assigns one brownie to each of the five people, but he then breaks one of the other two brownies into two pieces and the other into three pieces.

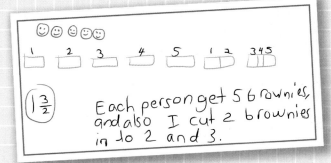

Philip's Work

Ask students like Philip about how they could be sure to give each person an *equal* share. Pose problems where it is possible to make equal shares using only wholes and halves, or wholes, halves, and fourths. Can they divide these groups of objects into equal shares? Can they write fractions and mixed numbers that represent these quantities?

Elena also distributes one whole brownie to each person but then does not attempt to divide the remaining two brownies into equal shares.

Elena's Work

Like Philip, her solution could work in a practical situation—give one brownie to each person and do not attempt to break up the other two brownies. However, her solution does not demonstrate whether she knows how to make equal shares of a whole. Would Elena solve this problem differently if she had six brownies to share equally among four people so that she could use only wholes and halves?

These students can benefit from continuing to play the *Fraction Cookie* game and solve sharing problems such as those on *Student Activity Book* page 29, using familiar contexts such as brownies or dollars.

Problem 2

Benchmarks addressed:

Benchmark 2: Identify equivalent fractions (e.g., $\frac{3}{6} = \frac{1}{2}$ and $\frac{1}{3} = \frac{2}{6}$).

Benchmark 3: Find combinations of fractions that are equal to one and to other fractions (e.g., $\frac{3}{6} + \frac{1}{2} = 1$; $\frac{1}{6} + \frac{1}{6} = \frac{1}{3}$; and $\frac{1}{3} + \frac{1}{6} = \frac{1}{2}$).

In order to meet the benchmarks, students' work should show that they can:

• Determine whether the two fractions combined equal 1 whole.

Benchmark 2 is difficult to assess as students' ability to recognize equivalent fractions is often embedded in their work. This benchmark is assessed by observation in Investigation 2, but many students will show in this problem that they recognize $\frac{2}{4} = \frac{1}{2}$.

> **2.** Each bag holds 24 apples. Kim collected $\frac{1}{3}$ of a bag. Philip collected $\frac{2}{4}$ of a bag. If they put all their apples together, would Kim and Philip have 1 whole bag?

▲ **Resource Masters, M19**

Meeting the Benchmarks

Students who meet the benchmark use correct reasoning to conclude that Kim's and Philip's apples will not fill a whole bag. Some students use only the fractions $\frac{1}{3}$ and $\frac{2}{4}$ in their solutions, and other students find the fractional parts of 24. Most students represent each fraction with a drawing, although a few may reason about the quantities without a drawing. Some students know that $\frac{2}{4}$ is equal to $\frac{1}{2}$ and so will not even identify fourths of 24.

Jung uses pattern blocks to show that $\frac{1}{3} + \frac{1}{2}$ does not equal one whole. Jung uses the red trapezoid as $\frac{2}{4}$, demonstrating that she recognizes the equivalence of the fractions, $\frac{1}{2}$ and $\frac{2}{4}$.

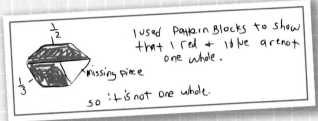

Jung's Work

Adam draws 24 circles to represent apples and puts a large circle around 12 of them. He knows that 12 apples is $\frac{1}{2}$ of 24 apples. At the top of his paper, he draws 24 apples in a row and divides them into three equal groups to determine how many are $\frac{1}{3}$ of 24 apples. He then shows that $\frac{1}{2} + \frac{1}{3}$ is not one whole because there are four apples left over.

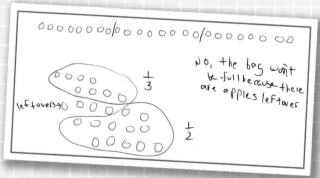

Adam's Work

Some students may show on a rectangle that $\frac{1}{2}$ of the area plus $\frac{1}{3}$ of the area is not the full rectangle. Also, a few students may use reasoning without any representations.

The following example shows that Becky recognizes that $\frac{2}{4} = \frac{1}{2}$. She also concludes that if $\frac{1}{3}$ is added to $\frac{1}{2}$, it is less than one.

> I know that $\frac{2}{4}$ is the same as $\frac{1}{2}$. And $\frac{1}{2} + \frac{1}{2} = 1$ so $\frac{1}{2} + \frac{1}{3}$ is NOT 1 because $\frac{1}{3}$ is less than $\frac{1}{2}$.

Becky's Work

Partially Meeting the Benchmarks

Finding fractions of 24 may be challenging because 24 is larger than the other numbers students work with in the unit. Some students may incorrectly identify the number of apples in each fractional part. They may correctly conclude that $\frac{1}{3} + \frac{2}{4}$ is less than one, but the numbers they base this on are incorrect.

For example, Oscar incorrectly identifies $\frac{2}{4}$ of 24 as 8 (it is not evident how he arrived at 8, but some students add $4 + 4$ because the denominator is 4). Oscar uses excellent reasoning about fractional quantities: that $\frac{2}{4} + \frac{1}{3}$ is less than one because $\frac{2}{4} + \frac{1}{2} = 1$ and $\frac{1}{3}$ is less than $\frac{1}{2}$. Oscar correctly answers the question "Is $\frac{2}{4} + \frac{1}{3}$ one whole?" but he should be asked to clarify his thinking about identifying $\frac{2}{4}$ of 24. Can he find $\frac{1}{4}$? Does he know that it has to be one of four equal pieces? Does he notice the equivalence of $\frac{2}{4}$ and $\frac{1}{2}$?

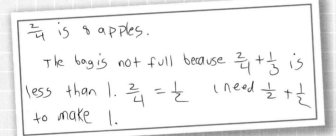

$\frac{2}{4}$ is 8 apples.

The bag is not full because $\frac{2}{4} + \frac{1}{3}$ is less than 1. $\frac{2}{4} = \frac{1}{2}$ I need $\frac{1}{2} + \frac{1}{2}$ to make 1.

Oscar's Work

Not Meeting the Benchmarks

Some students cannot identify fractions of a group of objects and/or cannot combine fractions by using reasoning or a representation. These students need more time using rectangles and pattern blocks to identify and combine fractional parts.

Elena relies only on a drawing of fractions on a rectangle. Her drawing is not accurate, and she incorrectly concludes that they equal one whole. It would be useful to ask Elena to show $\frac{2}{4}$ on one rectangle and $\frac{1}{3}$ on another to determine whether she understands that fractions are equal pieces of a whole.

Elena's Work

Nicholas demonstrates confusion about how to find fractional parts of a group. He incorrectly identifies $\frac{1}{3}$ of 24 as 3, and $\frac{1}{4}$ of 24 as 4. He does not yet understand what a fraction represents. He is trying to interpret fractions by drawing on his experience with whole numbers. In this case, he decides that $\frac{1}{3}$ means a group of three objects and that $\frac{1}{4}$ means a group of four objects. He is correct that the bag is not full, but it is clear that he is not making sense of what the notation represents.

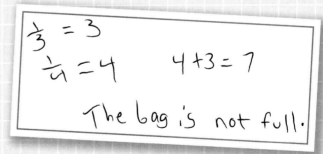

$\frac{1}{3} = 3$

$\frac{1}{4} = 4$ $\qquad$ $4 + 3 = 7$

The bag is not full.

Nicholas's Work

Nicholas should have continued experiences with the activities in this unit, particularly with dividing wholes and groups into equal parts and using fraction notation to represent his solutions. He should continue to use representations such as rectangle "brownies" and pattern blocks to help him to visualize the results of dividing a whole group into equal parts.

Seven Brownies, Four People

The teacher observes students as they divide seven brownies equally among four people in Session 1.5. As students work to find equal shares, the teacher helps them write each solution by using fractions. Later in the session, the students discuss how they can be sure that all of these fractions and fraction expressions are equivalent.

Becky: First, each person would get one.

Jung: But because there were only three left, we can't give another whole one out.

Becky: We can give a half to each person.

Jung: And we still have one left over. And we can't just divide it in half because there are four people.

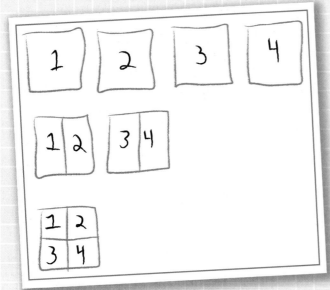

Jung's Work

Becky: So we divide it into quarters and add a quarter to each half. That is one and a third.

Teacher: This is what one third looks like [draws a rectangle and splits it into thirds], and one and one third would look like one and one of those pieces.

Becky: So what would a half plus a fourth be?

Teacher: That is the question! Let's draw what each person would get. Draw me one half plus one fourth.

Becky: [draws a new picture in which she shades in one half and one fourth in the same whole] It's $\frac{3}{4}$.

Becky's Work

Jung: That makes sense, Becky, because there are two fourths in one half, remember?

Becky: So each person gets one and a half and a quarter.

The teacher writes the following on the board:

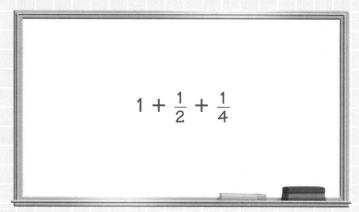

$$1 + \frac{1}{2} + \frac{1}{4}$$

The teacher moves to another pair and asks them how they shared the seven brownies.

Ines: We gave one whole to each person and then split the three brownies into four parts, one for each person.

Teacher: Tell me what to do to the picture.

Ines: Split the three brownies with a line this way [makes a vertical motion] and this way [makes a horizontal motion]. Now each person gets a piece from each brownie.

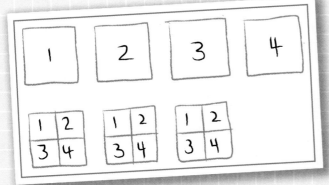

Ines' Work

Teacher: What size pieces are these?

Kim: Quarters. Fourths.

Teacher: How much brownie does each person get?

Kim: One whole brownie and three of the fourths pieces.

The teacher writes the following on the board:

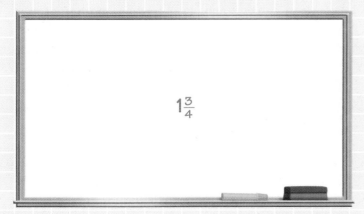

The teacher moves on to another group that has cut all their brownies into fourths.

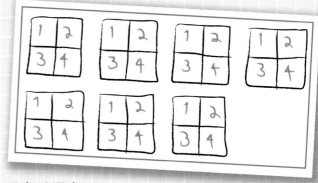

Kathryn's Work

Teacher: Why did you cut up all of your brownies?

Kathryn: There are four people sharing so we knew that we needed fourths.

Oscar: So each person gets seven of the fourths.

Oscar points to his paper which shows: $\frac{1}{4} + \frac{1}{4} + \frac{1}{4} + \frac{1}{4} + \frac{1}{4} + \frac{1}{4} + \frac{1}{4} = \frac{7}{4}$.

As students work, the teacher listens to see whether they understand that fractions are equal pieces of a whole and whether they can distinguish between halves, fourths, and thirds. The teacher writes these different notations on the board for the following discussion, in which students consider how different notations ($\frac{7}{4}$, $1\frac{3}{4}$, and $1 + \frac{1}{2} + \frac{1}{4}$) can represent the same portion of brownies.

Dialogue Box

Playing the *Fraction Cookie* Game

The class is playing the *Fraction Cookie* game. The teacher listens in as Elena and Gil talk to each other while they play. She occasionally asks the students questions about the moves they are making.

Elena: I rolled one sixth, so I need a green.

She takes a green triangle and fits it onto one of the hexagons on her copy of the Hexagon Cookies page.

Gil: I got one half. So I'll take a red. And I can trade in my two reds for one yellow.

He makes this trade and places a yellow block on the hexagon he has just filled in on his Hexagon Cookies page.

Teacher: Gil, why did you trade your two reds for a yellow?

Gil: I know that they're both halves, and two halves are one whole.

Elena: Okay, my turn. I got one third. That's a blue. Can I do any trades? I could trade my green and blue for a red.

Teacher: How come, Elena?

Elena: They fit together to make the same shape as the red, like this. [She demonstrates.]

Teacher: So what does that tell you about the fractions that these shapes represent?

Elena: That they go together. If you put a third and a sixth together, you get a half.

Gil: If you had two blues, you could trade them for four greens.

Elena: But that would be more pieces, and I want less.

Gil: [as he rolls the fraction cube] Two thirds, that's two blues. I'm trading two blues and two greens for two reds.

Elena: Just make it a yellow.

Teacher: How do you know that all those pieces will make a yellow hexagon?

Gil: Yes, it does. And it's the same as if I trade the two greens for another blue.

Teacher: Can you tell me why?

Gil: Three blues—that's three thirds—it's the same as two halves, and they're all just one yellow. But we ran out of yellows. I'll just color in a yellow and then I'll know I made a whole.

The teacher is helping these students focus on the pattern block pieces as representations of fractions. Both students are moving back and forth between naming the pieces by color and by their fraction names. As they do this, they are developing a strong visual image of how thirds, sixths, and halves combine to make a whole. They are also becoming familiar with a number of basic fraction equivalencies, such as the relationship between thirds and sixths.

Dialogue Box

Sharing Dollars

In this Dialogue Box, students are working on the Sharing Dollars problems on *Student Activity Book* page 30. They are comparing the answers they found by using the calculator with the original answers they found in the previous session.

Jane: One dollar divided among four people . . . [she enters 1.00 ÷ 4 into the calculator]. I know that it's twenty-five cents, and look, it's 0.25. I don't know what the zero is for but I see it whenever I get a decimal on the calculator.

Keisha: What about two dollars shared among eight people?

Jane: It's the same. Twenty-five cents.

Keisha: What do you mean, it's the same?

Jane: Eight is twice four, so I double both things, so the answer should be the same. Let's share it out with quarters. [They both work to share eight quarters among four people and see that it is the same.] See, before you had $1.00 for four, and now it is just another dollar for another four.

Keisha: Let me do it on the calculator. Zero point two five! What about two dollars shared among four people? When I spread out the money, I got two quarters for each person.

Jane: Let's do it on the calculator. [She presses the numbers.] I get 0.5.

Keisha: So two quarters is fifty cents, which you write 0.50. Why is it just 0.5 on the calculator?

Jane: I don't know. But I added 0.5 and 0.5 and I got one. So 0.5 is half of one and 50 is half of 100 so maybe it is the same thing.

In this activity, students are beginning to notice some fraction and decimal equivalents. By the end of this activity and the Sharing With and Without a Calculator activity that students work on in the next session, students should recognize that $\frac{1}{2} = 0.5$ and $\frac{1}{4} = 0.25$ (some students also recognize that $\frac{3}{4} = 0.75$). Keisha and Jane are finding out that there is another way to write numbers that are less than one; that is, parts (or fractions) of dollars can also be represented by decimals (0.5, 0.25). Although it may not be clear to students that the notation for money is related to tenths and hundredths of a dollar (i.e., one penny is one hundredth of a dollar and 25 pennies is twenty-five hundredths of a dollar), many students know that coins are parts of one whole dollar. Using this context, students begin to understand the connection between $\frac{1}{4}$ and 0.25.

Student Math Handbook

The *Student Math Handbook* pages related to this unit are pictured on the following pages. This book is designed to be used flexibly: as a resource for students doing classwork, as a book students can take home for reference while doing homework and playing math games with their families, and as a reference for families to better understand the work their children are doing in class.

When students take the *Student Math Handbook* home, they and their families can discuss these pages together to reinforce or enhance students' understanding of the mathematical concepts and games in this unit.

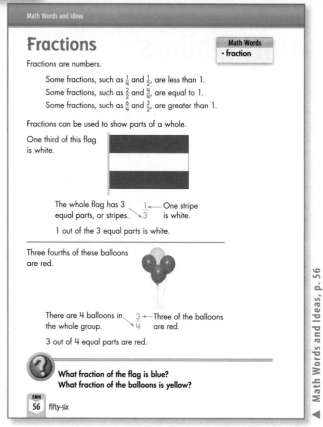

Fractions

Math Words
· fraction

Fractions are numbers.

Some fractions, such as $\frac{1}{4}$ and $\frac{1}{2}$, are less than 1.
Some fractions, such as $\frac{2}{2}$ and $\frac{4}{4}$, are equal to 1.
Some fractions, such as $\frac{6}{4}$ and $\frac{3}{2}$, are greater than 1.

Fractions can be used to show parts of a whole.

One third of this flag is white.

The whole flag has 3 equal parts, or stripes. $\frac{1}{3}$ ← One stripe is white.

1 out of the 3 equal parts is white.

Three fourths of these balloons are red.

There are 4 balloons in the whole group. $\frac{3}{4}$ ← Three of the balloons are red.

3 out of 4 equal parts are red.

? What fraction of the flag is blue?
What fraction of the balloons is yellow?

SMH
56 fifty-six

Math Words and Ideas, p. 56 ►

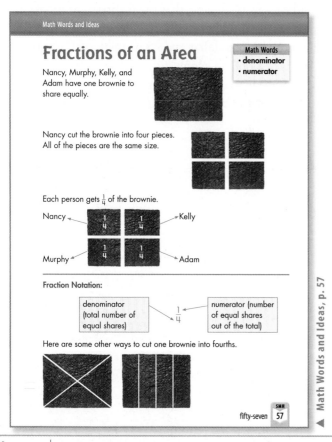

Fractions of an Area

Math Words
· denominator
· numerator

Nancy, Murphy, Kelly, and Adam have one brownie to share equally.

Nancy cut the brownie into four pieces. All of the pieces are the same size.

Each person gets $\frac{1}{4}$ of the brownie.

Nancy → | $\frac{1}{4}$ | $\frac{1}{4}$ | ← Kelly

Murphy → | $\frac{1}{4}$ | $\frac{1}{4}$ | ← Adam

Fraction Notation:

denominator (total number of equal shares) → $\frac{1}{4}$ ← numerator (number of equal shares out of the total)

Here are some other ways to cut one brownie into fourths.

fifty-seven SMH **57**

◄ Math Words and Ideas, p. 57

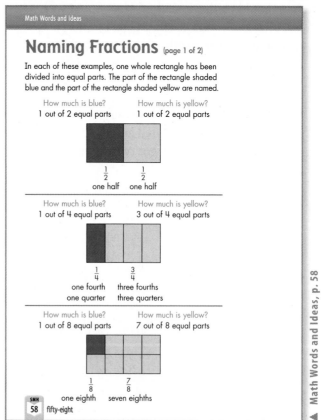

Naming Fractions (page 1 of 2)

In each of these examples, one whole rectangle has been divided into equal parts. The part of the rectangle shaded blue and the part of the rectangle shaded yellow are named.

How much is blue?   How much is yellow?
1 out of 2 equal parts   1 out of 2 equal parts

$\frac{1}{2}$ $\frac{1}{2}$
one half   one half

How much is blue?   How much is yellow?
1 out of 4 equal parts   3 out of 4 equal parts

$\frac{1}{4}$ $\frac{3}{4}$
one fourth   three fourths
one quarter   three quarters

How much is blue?   How much is yellow?
1 out of 8 equal parts   7 out of 8 equal parts

$\frac{1}{8}$ $\frac{7}{8}$
SMH   seven eighths
58 fifty-eight one eighth

◄ Math Words and Ideas, p. 58

Naming Fractions (page 2 of 2)

How much is blue?   How much is yellow?
1 out of 3 equal parts   2 out of 3 equal parts

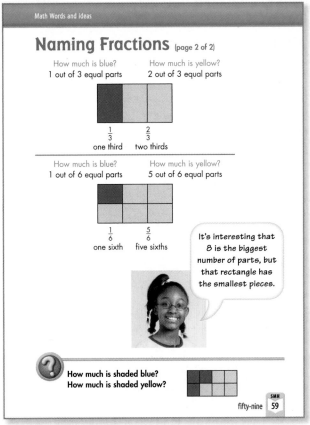

$\frac{1}{3}$ $\frac{2}{3}$
one third   two thirds

How much is blue?   How much is yellow?
1 out of 6 equal parts   5 out of 6 equal parts

$\frac{1}{6}$ $\frac{5}{6}$
one sixth   five sixths

It's interesting that 8 is the biggest number of parts, but that rectangle has the smallest pieces.

? How much is shaded blue?
How much is shaded yellow?

◄ Math Words and Ideas, p. 59

Fractions of a Group of Objects

Three people share 15 apples equally.
Each person gets $\frac{1}{3}$ of the apples.

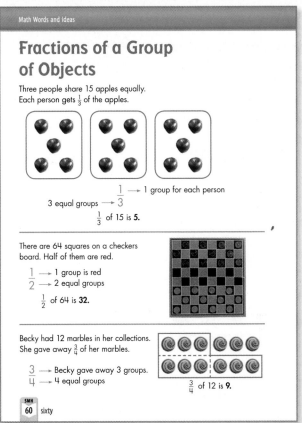

$\frac{1}{3}$ → 1 group for each person

3 equal groups → $\frac{1}{3}$

$\frac{1}{3}$ of 15 is **5.**

There are 64 squares on a checkers board. Half of them are red.

$\frac{1}{2}$ → 1 group is red
→ 2 equal groups

$\frac{1}{2}$ of 64 is **32.**

Becky had 12 marbles in her collections. She gave away $\frac{3}{4}$ of her marbles.

$\frac{3}{4}$ → Becky gave away 3 groups.
→ 4 equal groups

$\frac{3}{4}$ of 12 is **9.**

◄ Math Words and Ideas, p. 60

Using Fractions for Quantities Greater Than One (page 1 of 2)

Math Words
• mixed number

Edwin and Pilar solved a problem about people and brownies. Each person's share is greater than one.

Two people shared 3 brownies equally. How much does each person get?

Edwin's Solution:

First I gave one whole brownie to each person.

There was one brownie left. I split it into 2 equal pieces and gave each person one-half.

Each person gets $1\frac{1}{2}$.

A mixed number has a whole number part and a fractional part.

whole number → $1\frac{1}{2}$ ← fraction

one and one-half

◄ Math Words and Ideas, p. 61

Using Fractions for Quantities Greater Than One (page 2 of 2)

Pilar's Solution:

I cut all the brownies into 2 equal pieces. Each person gets 1 piece, or half, of each brownie.

Each person gets $\frac{3}{2}$.

$\frac{1}{2} + \frac{1}{2} + \frac{1}{2} = \frac{3}{2}$

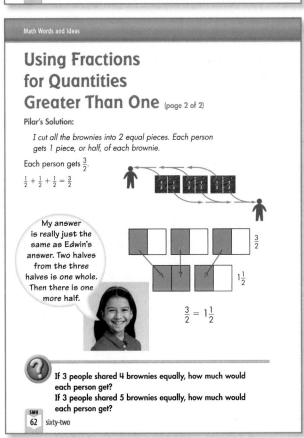

My answer is really just the same as Edwin's answer. Two halves from the three halves is one whole. Then there is one more half.

$\frac{3}{2}$

$1\frac{1}{2}$

$\frac{3}{2} = 1\frac{1}{2}$

? If 3 people shared 4 brownies equally, how much would each person get?
If 3 people shared 5 brownies equally, how much would each person get?

◄ Math Words and Ideas, p. 62

Equivalent Fractions

Math Words
- equivalent fractions

Different fractions that name the same amount are called equivalent fractions.

Keith used pattern blocks to show some equivalent fractions.

$\frac{3}{6} = \frac{1}{2}$

$\frac{1}{3} = \frac{2}{6}$

Jane showed some other equivalent fractions by using rectangles.

$\frac{1}{2} = \frac{2}{4}$

$\frac{3}{4} = \frac{6}{8}$

Chris showed that $\frac{1}{2}$ and $\frac{4}{8}$ are equivalent fractions by using a group of 8 cubes.

Four out of eight of these cubes are red.
Half of these cubes are red. $\frac{4}{8} = \frac{1}{2}$

? What two equivalent fractions name the portion of red cubes?

sixty-three **SMH 63**

▲ Math Words and Ideas, p. 63

Fraction Combinations

These students wrote equations to show the fraction parts and totals for each of these pictures.

Chiang	Keisha
$\frac{3}{6} + \frac{1}{2} = 1$	$\frac{1}{3} + \frac{1}{6} = \frac{1}{2}$
Denzel	Murphy
$\frac{1}{2} + \frac{2}{4} = 1$	$\frac{1}{6} + \frac{1}{6} = \frac{1}{3}$

? Use pattern blocks to find more fraction combinations that equal 1.

1    $\frac{1}{2}$ $\frac{1}{3}$ $\frac{1}{6}$

SMH 64 sixty-four

▲ Math Words and Ideas, p. 64

Fractions and Decimals That Are Equal

Math Words
- decimal
- decimal point

Numbers that include decimal points are called decimals. Some numbers can be written as either fractions or decimals.

0.65   MARCH MARATHON 26.2 miles $9.75

These problems can be answered by using fractions or decimals.

Four people share one dollar equally. How much money does each person get?

Fraction answer:
Each person gets $\frac{1}{4}$ dollar.

Decimal answer:
Each person gets $0.25.

$\frac{1}{4} = 0.25$

Two people share three dollars equally. How much money does each person get?

Fraction answer:
Each person gets $1\frac{1}{2}$ dollars.

Decimal answer:
Each person gets $1.50.

$\frac{1}{2} = 0.50$

sixty-five **SMH 65**

▲ Math Words and Ideas, p. 65

Fraction Cookie (page 1 of 2)

You need
- pattern blocks
- fraction number cubes (2 in one color and 1 in a different color)
- *Hexagon Cookies*

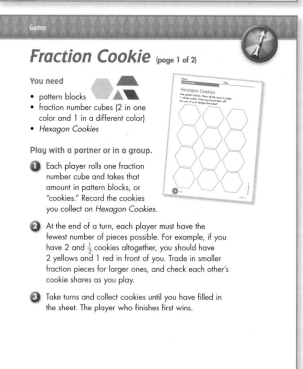

Play with a partner or in a group.

1 Each player rolls one fraction number cube and takes that amount in pattern blocks, or "cookies." Record the cookies you collect on *Hexagon Cookies*.

2 At the end of a turn, each player must have the fewest number of pieces possible. For example, if you have 2 and $\frac{1}{2}$ cookies altogether, you should have 2 yellows and 1 red in front of you. Trade in smaller fraction pieces for larger ones, and check each other's cookie shares as you play.

3 Take turns and collect cookies until you have filled in the sheet. The player who finishes first wins.

SMH G11

▲ Games, G11

Games

Fraction Cookie (page 2 of 2)

Intermediate: Adding Fraction Cookies
(two fraction number cubes)

Each player rolls two fraction number cubes, adds the two amounts, and collects that amount of cookies in pattern blocks. Continue to trade so that you always have the fewest pieces possible at the end of your turn. Play continues until players have filled up one sheet; players may also agree to fill two sheets in this version.

Advanced: Adding and Subtracting Fraction Cookies
(three fraction number cubes)

Each player rolls two fraction number cubes of one color and a third fraction number cube of a different color, adds the amounts on the first two cubes, and then subtracts the amount on the third cube from his or her cookie collection. Continue to trade so that you always have the fewest pieces possible at the end of your turn. In this version of the game, start with two whole hexagon cookies so you do not run out when you subtract. The first player to get four cookies (or any other number agreed on) wins.

SMH
G12

▲ Games, G12

Index